The Modern Timber House in the UK
New Paradigms and Technologies

Peter Wilson

A UK registered architect, Peter Wilson's work for the past two decades has focused on the the use of timber in architecture and construction. During this time he has been instrumental in the development and promotion of architectural awards, design competitions, lectures, seminars, conferences, publications and built demonstration projects that highlight innovation and design excellence in the use of timber. Prior to his current position as director of Timber Design Initiatives Ltd, he headed the Wood Studio research centre within Edinburgh Napier University's Institute for Sustainable Construction, in which capacity he led a major EU-funded project to develop a range of new products and construction systems from UK grown timber. He writes regularly for a range of specialist journals and magazines on the application of advanced timber technologies and previously authored *New Timber Architecture in Scotland*, documenting the transformative use of timber in the country's built environment in the early years of this century.

arcamedia

Published in 2017 by Arcamedia Ltd
90a Constitution Street
Edinburgh EH6 6RP
Scotland
T +44 (0)131 554 8643
E arcamedia@icloud.com
W www.arcamedia.co.uk

British Library Cataloguing-in-Publication Data

A catalogue record for this book is available from the British Library.

ISBN 978-1-904320-09-8 (pbk)

Editor: Judith Kelly

Layout, cover design and typography: Alan Mairs

Printed and bound by Base Print Solutions

Cover photograph: Howe Farm, Buckinghamshire (2016)
IPT Architects
Photographer: Andy Spain

Acknowledgements / Credits

The Modern Timber House in the UK complements a series of conferences that were promoted by Wood for Good during 2016. These events were designed to encourage greater use of timber in the construction of housing and provided highly original, state-of-the-art contributions from leading architects, engineers and housing managers on new approaches being taken in this field. They also offered important pointers and possible solutions on how current housing shortages might be effectively tackled, information that provided the starting point of research for this book. The decisions as to which projects should be selected for inclusion and the chapters they are discussed in were thus made by the author alone, as was the development of the overall structure and content of the book itself. All of the statements, opinions and interpretations as expressed in the text should not, therefore, be read as carrying the endorsement of any party that has supported the production of this publication. Hopefully, any questions that may arise over these decisions will not affect readers' appreciation and understanding of the many diverse approaches now being applied to the design of housing or of the range of timber technologies used to achieve the outstanding results highlighted in the following pages.

Bringing this work to fruition has not been a solitary exercise: throughout its gestation, Andy Leitch, Policy Adviser at Forestry Commission Scotland has been a constant support and indeed, without his encouragement, this book might never have been started, whilst Roland Stiven has played a patient liaison role on behalf of the Board of Wood for Good, all of the members of which deserve considerable credit for their vision in commissioning this book. Thanks too, need to be given to three people who have been instrumental in achieving the high quality of the final product in front of you: Alan Mairs for bringing his design experience to bear on the extensive text and vast array of images he was confronted with and which he has turned into an easily accessible and visually striking document; Judith Kelly for applying her journalistic knowledge and experience to the editing of several manuscript drafts before permitting the final version to progress into print; and to Steve Thorburn of Baseprint Solutions who has guided the book through the paper selection, print and production processes to deliver the finely finished publication you have in your hands.

Ultimately, this book would not have been possible without the generous contribution of time and material from two particular professional groups - the architectural practices whose work is represented in these pages and the photographers whose outstanding images have captured the essence of the featured projects. The members of these two groups are listed in the rear of this book and it is their collective commitment and passion to produce work of outstanding quality that has made the writing of The Modern Timber House in the UK a pleasure and an inspiration.

Finally, I wish to thank my wife for the extraordinary patience and support she has shown to me through the long months of work that have been necessary to bring this book to fruition: Alison, this is for you.

Peter Wilson, September 2017

Contents

**Hannibal Gardens,
Stepney Green,
London** (2012)
Peter Barber Architects
Photographer: Morley von
Sternberg

Preface
Building: Dwelling: (Re)Thinking

The title above unashamedly paraphrases that of the seminal lecture, *Building, Dwelling, Thinking* (1951) by German philosopher, Martin Heidegger, on what it means to dwell and build: one of the central tenets expounded in the text, explores the idea that when building becomes associated with the mere construction of houses, it becomes habitual and we tend to forget what we mean by building (as dwelling). So much of today's discussion about housing revolves around shortages and speed of delivery of new homes: the focus is on overall numbers and timescales and, arguably, with very little attention devoted to the quality of the homes being provided, or to their contribution to the cultures of the UKs local and regional built environments. Nor does it address what might be regarded as niche markets for which there are considerable, but perhaps less obviously apparent, demand. And then there are the many interpretations of what is meant by 'affordable housing' and how the multifarious needs within this sector might be better met.

Hence 'rethinking' since, inherent in a book entitled *'The Modern Timber House in the UK'*, is the implication of some reconsideration of what has gone before. Mankind's earliest constructed dwellings were formed from wood and largely continued to be so until only a few centuries ago. That the evolution of construction since the Industrial Revolution progressively moved the domestic architecture of the UK away from the use of indigenous, locally available materials and towards manufactured elements and the economic benefits of serial production is not in question, nor is the virtue of this as a response to ongoing shifts in population from the countryside to the employment opportunities available in larger towns and cities. Manifestly evident, however, from the timeline that stretches between the late 18th and late 20th centuries, is the progressive decline not only in the use of wood to form new homes, coupled with a developing amnesia about how wood can be fashioned to do so and the consequent de-emphasis on maintaining the country's valuable human resource of carpentry, joinery and other manual construction skills.

This is not to hark back to some William Morris' style, dream-like golden age of human creativity and endeavour but to recognise that, in these early years of the 21st century, concerns about climate change and global ecology have moved inexorably to the foreground and that, almost in parallel with these changed imperatives, something of a renaissance in the use of timber in construction has become increasingly apparent. Arguably, this is most evident in the interest being shown in the design opportunities associated with a new generation of engineered and modified timber products: it is now possible to build large-scale structures with wood that were never achievable before. To do so has required greater understanding of the mechanical properties of the many different species of timber that are in common use, a learning curve that has taken many architects, engineers and other construction professionals into new and, for some, unexpectedly advanced areas of technological development. As such, the integration

Old Bearhurst,
East Sussex (2011)
Duggan Morris Architects
Photographer: James Brittain

of timber into design thinking has moved well beyond the fashionable (with the often gratuitous application of timber cladding on housing found in standard developments as an obvious example) and into the very structure and fabric of new buildings.

The primary purpose of this book, therefore, is to show the many facets of timber products and systems that are being applied in the design and construction of new housing in the UK today. Its second motivation is to encourage not only greater use of timber in the country's domestic architecture but, by helping to engender a better understanding of how this endlessly diverse resource can be used, it is hoped that design professionals who read it will wish to apply this knowledge in any new commissions they receive for housing projects. Having done so, and with the confidence and experience thus gained, the next and most exciting stage will surely be the application of serious creative thinking on how the planet's foremost renewable material might best be employed in the delivery of large numbers of new dwellings.

To return now to Heidegger and the ideas contained in *Building*, *Dwelling*, *Thinking*: conceiving new dimensions to the way we create housing is not just about the regulations and technicalities of construction, it is also very much about the ways in which we reconsider the nature of dwelling. Heidegger's thesis evokes recollection of another celebrated three-word proclamation from history: the advice to builders from the Roman architect, Marcus Vitruvius Pollio, to ensure *Firmitas*, *Utilitas*, *Venustas* in all their constructions, i.e. *Firmness*, *Commodity and Delight*. It is the last of these that this two-part book wishes most to encourage amongst the many parties engaged in house building in the UK today: to take as much delight in the use of timber as is shown in the examples included within the pages here and, in doing so, to bring absolute and enduring delight to those who dwell.

**The Cedar Lodges,
Winchester, Hampshire** (2015)
Adam Knibb Architects
Photographer: Martin Gardner

Foreword

We live in extraordinary times of change and challenge. Environmental catastrophes in different parts of the world bear witness to a climate warmed by increasing carbon dioxide emissions: peoples' homes and lives are impacted by natural phenomena made more severe by our emissions. In the UK the housing crisis has put the cost of buying a home out of reach for more and more people. These twin challenges, while significant, can be responded to creatively, individually as well as collectively and the way we build our homes can play a unique role in doing so. Our homes are the places where we feel safe, they provide us with shelter, they are where we bring up our children, host our friends and, for those lucky enough to be able to build their own home, they are the places where our creativity can be expressed and celebrated.

This book showcases the beauty, strength and versatility of timber and how it can play an ever-increasing role in addressing the combined challenges of climate change and housing need. It demonstrates, too, just how innovative designers and engineers can be in developing new systems and solutions using a material that predates our existence on the planet. Timber enables us to build the most energy-efficient of homes to help us minimise the use of fossil fuels and, consequently, our emissions. A naturally renewable material, it not only has one of the lowest carbon footprints of any construction material, it is also made of the carbon that trees absorb from the atmosphere as they grow: we can literally build with carbon, capturing and storing it in the fabric of our homes.

Wood for Good is the UK's promotion campaign to encourage more use of timber design and construction. We provide education and training resources for architects, engineers, designers, specifiers, contractors, developers, housing associations, local authorities and policy makers and run seminars and debates across the UK on innovation, sustainability and emerging market trends in the use of wood. Our current campaign responds not only to the housing crisis but also introduces people to the idea of Custom Build, the UK Government's programme that, underpinned by Community Right to Build legislation, enables any of us to consider building our own homes. With the generous support of Forestry Commission Scotland, Wood for Good commissioned The Modern Timber House in The UK to highlight the many ways we can do this with timber. The book is not only timely, therefore: it is also a beautiful collation of homes made from wood. It intelligently sets out why the modern timber house has its roots in a rich architectural heritage and reveals to professionals and lay people alike that the future for our homes will have timber at its heart. I hope you will enjoy it and am certain you will find it a source of inspiration.

With its publication, my role as chair of Wood for Good has come to an end I am delighted to be handing the baton over to David Birkbeck, CEO of Design for Homes. I am certain the Wood for Good campaign will go from strength to strength under his guidance.

Craig White, Chair of Wood for Good

Introduction

Transformative Innovation

It is almost a decade since the Stadthaus, a nine storey residential tower block in the London Borough of Hackney, dramatically changed political and public perceptions of what might be achieved in the construction of new housing in the UK through the use of modern engineered timber products. Constructed almost entirely from cross laminated timber (CLT) it was, at the time of its completion in 2008, the tallest timber residential building in the world. The technology itself has been commercially available since the beginning of this century, but its pioneering use in the delivery of sustainable high-rise, high-density housing was undoubtedly a game-changer. It also opened the door to wider industry interest in the use of CLT as well as other developments in timber products and systems as a possible means of resolving the increasing shortage of new housing in the UK. *The Modern Timber House in the UK* addresses the many ways in which different timber technologies have been applied in residential design and construction over the course of the past ten years and concludes with a review of where the many architectural solutions and design and technical innovations documented may point towards in the future.

Any new book on the design and quality of new housing in the UK would, however, be failing in its purpose if it did not take into account the economic, environmental, political and social factors that have impacted upon the country's construction industry during the period it explores. *The Modern Timber House in the UK* embraces the years 2007-17, a period that began immediately before the economic crash that sent the country's construction industry into deep and long-lasting economic recession, and ends its survey in July 2017 with the publication of the UK Government's response to 'Modernise or Die', the Farmer Review of the UK Construction Labour Model (October 2016)—an incisive but damning report it had itself commissioned and one with major implications for the housebuilding sector.

The Farmer Review is not an isolated *cri de cœur*: throughout the past decade—and even before—many official documents have been published with the intent of improving the workings of the UK construction industry and of the housebuilding sector in particular, the enduring impression from all being of an ever-growing deficiency (widely referred to as a 'crisis') in new housing provision, perhaps best illustrated by the title of the Department for Local Government and Communities' own publication, *Fixing our Broken Housing Market* (February 2017). The problems it and other publications repeatedly highlight are well known and can be grouped into four broad areas: a continually growing, nationwide demand for affordably-priced new housing; the availability and cost of land for housebuilding; the availability—or lack—of development and mortgage finance; and increasing consumer awareness and concern over environmental issues and rising energy costs. A fifth category might be added: that of construction quality, within which resides a range of questions as to the industry's current ability to deliver Government targets on numbers and timescales for new house completions.

Stadthaus,
Murray Grove,
London Borough of Hackney
(2008)
Waugh Thistleton Architects
Photographer: Will Pryce

1

These issues are addressed across the course of the fourteen chapters that follow, in each case with examples of how timber products and systems have been—and are being—used to deliver new forms of housing to very high standards of construction, energy efficiency and environmental responsiveness.

The housebuilding sector's inability to produce enough houses at the speed required is hardly new: long wedded to traditional building methods, the onsite, brick and block process that predominates in England and Wales is slow, weather-dependent and reliant on a diminishing skill base. This problem was exacerbated by the sudden cessation in building contracts that hit UK construction in 2008 and which resulted in many experienced site workers leaving the industry, never to return. Their disappearance has, until recently, been mitigated by the availability of skilled labour from abroad, but political events appear to be reversing this direction of travel and have further exposed what, currently, are possibly the industry's two biggest weaknesses: the failure to invest in skills training and the reluctance, until very recently, to make significant progress towards the use of Modern Methods of Construction (MMC) and offsite manufacture (OSM).

These are not issues, it should be said, that affect different parts of the UK timber processing, manufacturing and construction sectors in the same ways. Prefabricated, platform timber frame construction has long been the preferred modus operandi of house builders in Scotland, where upwards of 70% of new housing up to seven storeys in height is produced by this method. The benefits of accurate, factory-based manufacture (explored in Chapter 2—The Framed and Panelled Timber House) are many, with the technology increasingly infiltrating the larger market in England and Wales and where, measured in total numbers of house completions, more timber frame dwellings are now being built than in the smaller, essentially mature, Scottish market. The use of structural insulated panels (SIPs) too, has risen significantly but, currently, the fastest growth in the use of timber products in UK house building is arguably in the use of cross laminated timber in combination with other engineered products such as glulam and laminated veneer lumber (LVL).

In this new world of advanced timber technologies, offsite manufacturing processes are able to produce extremely accurate, large format panels into which door and window openings are pre-cut and channels for cables and pipes pre-routed. Whilst this reduces onsite construction time and minimises the number of site operatives and specialist skills required to manipulate and fix the CLT floor, wall and roof plates, it has also enabled greater design and manufacturing development of fully-fitted volumetric units that, on delivery to site, can be quickly assembled into finished buildings. Until relatively recently, the use of such modules in the UK was mostly confined to repetitive building types such as hotels and student housing, but more flexible timber-based systems continue to emerge—so much so that Legal & General (L&G), a major UK financial institution, has recently established a subsidiary company, L&G Housing, and invested in a 51,000 sq/m cross laminated timber manufacturing and module assembly facility that is intended to produce around 3,500 modular housing units per year. The first prototypes homes have already been launched.

Progress to precision offsite manufacturing on this scale aims to impact upon the current gap between actual housing completions and government housing targets, as well as addressing the huge demand that exists for housing defined as 'affordable' (discussed in Chapter 5—The

Affordable Timber House). It also highlights the move towards faster mechanised fabrication processes, more akin to vehicle manufacture, but which respond positively to the imperatives of the Circular Economy, a domain in which timber's known sustainability and other construction-efficient credentials offer many advantages over other materials.

The Farmer Review also points to the likelihood of the UK seeing a decline in the available construction workforce of some 25% over the next 10 years and that such a decrease would render the industry incapable of delivering the infrastructure and housing the country so badly needs. This, the Review makes clear, is a scenario the UK has never faced before, with the tipping point likely to be reached within the next five to 10 years, at which point the symptoms will worsen and the decline become irreversible. Thus, the Review's inescapably insistent sub-title: ' Modernise or Die: Time to decide the industry's future', a forewarning compounded by the author's forensic spotlight being pointed at the industry's lack of innovation and collaboration, together with its almost non-existent research and development (R&D) culture. These are all areas in which current activity in the world of advanced timber technologies can be judged to score highly, but the frontiers need to be continually invested in and further developed for this rapidly expanding industry to remain strongly competitive with other sectors.

It is here, perhaps, that companies and organisations in the wider timber industry needs to become more collaborative and to share the expense of training a new and better skilled workforce. Inherent in this is the need to evolve a clear programme of cross-disciplinary career options in which personnel, once experienced, can see real opportunities for advancement and the possibility of secure, long-term and well-paid employment. The evidence of this book makes clear the benefits to be had when architects, engineers, processors, manufacturers and installers share ideas and knowledge, working together to produce innovative timber-based solutions, many of which—with further research and development—could potentially be rolled out more widely on a commercial basis.

Utilising digital technology lies at the heart of such endeavour and, with advances being made in this area in almost every other industry, the need for continuing investment is paramount. Farmer states that "the importance of Building Information Modelling (BIM) cannot be overestimated in the battle to modernise the construction industry" but goes on to point out that "investment in, and adoption of, BIM is being stymied, with some notable exceptions, by all of the issues highlighted already around lack of willingness to invest and collaborate and the inability to see the bigger picture business case." Here then is the opportunity for the timber industry and house builders to work in concert to become one of the notable exceptions referred to: encourage and support architects and engineers to use BIM in the development of timber-based housing projects and provide both these professions with a structured programme of Continuing Professional Education on all aspects of timber design and construction. The bigger picture business case for investment in these two areas is the creation of a bright new sustainable world of innovative, high quality housing formed from timber products and systems: transformative innovation is the process; outstanding built examples are the vehicles needed to convince others of the efficacy of timber construction. *The Modern Timber House in the UK* contains around 100 such paradigms, underpinned with a clear exposition of the technologies by which they have been delivered. This, then, is both a handbook for change in the way we think about housebuilding in the UK and a guidebook to the possibilities of implementation.

Part 1
Modern Timber Technologies

The phrase 'modern timber house' can be interpreted in many ways depending, at one extreme, upon individual perceptions of what a house made from wood might, or should, look like and, at the other, by a comprehensive knowledge of the range of timber technologies nowadays available. Modern versions of the archetypal log cabin are available in the form of a number of proprietary log-type systems that are imported and marketed in the UK. but proponents of sustainable timber construction may feel something is amiss in following this path since the timber employed is unlikely to have been grown and felled locally and consequently makes little or no cultural reference to indigenous construction traditions that have arisen from considerations of local climate, landscape and species availability. Whilst this publication is not about this particular form of construction, it does reference other traditional building technologies such as the use of green timber, box frames and post and beam structures, the latter two being precursors to modern timber frame and panelised systems.

'Modern Timber Technologies', therefore, provides background to the range of generic timber technologies that can be found in use today and which will re-emerge in various forms and combinations throughout this book. The sequence of information is, to some extent, chronological, beginning in Chapter 1 with the oldest and simplest form of timber construction: green timber, i.e.wood from trees that have been recently felled and which has not been dried before being used in the building process. Key to the inclusion of this particular construction method is the different, and increasingly innovative, ways in which this technology is being rediscovered and applied today.

What the term 'timber frame' means from a contemporary perspective follows and includes a summary of the offsite-manufactured panel systems that increasingly provide a substantial proportion of prefabricated housing systems. The various manifestations of the technologies embraced in Chapter 2 provide a significant element in the structural design of many of the conventional outputs of the UK housebuilding sector but, more often than not, are rendered invisible by the external or internal cladding materials fixed to them. These houses may be primarily constructed of timber, but since this is not apparent, the importance—and value—of timber usage in contemporary UK housebuilding is less well recognised than it should be. The example projects in this chapter aim to widen understanding of the construction and thermal efficiency of timber frame systems as well as the flexibility of these technologies.

Engineered, solid timber products and systems are relatively recent entrants to the UK housebuilding scene but their impact is expanding exponentially as more designers, specifiers and contractors gain experience of them in practice and recognise the many advantages they bring to the construction process. Many architects and engineers, however, have not yet had the opportunity to use one or more of these products and there is still considerable education to be carried out across the sector to better inform construction professionals, developers,

Edge Hill, Ponteland, Northumberland (2015)

Sutherland Hussey Harris Architects

Photographer: Colin Harris / SUHUHA

Carmarthen Place,
Bermondsey, London (2007)
Architects in Residence (AiR)
Photographer: Riko Hise

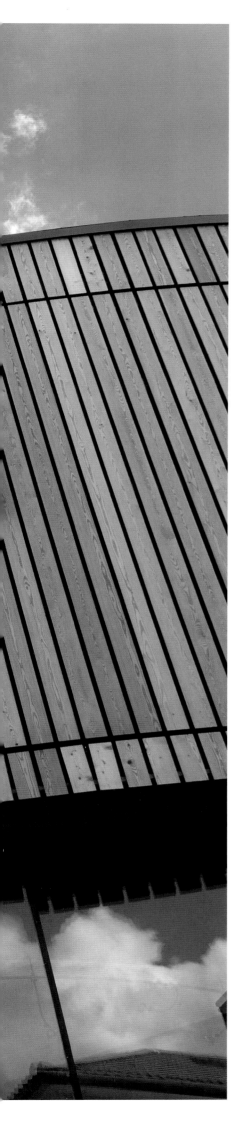

mortgage providers, insurers and regulatory authorities as to their mechanical properties and technical constraints, such as fire resistance, as well as the environmental credentials that together contribute to engineered timber's value to the Circular Economy. These products and systems come in glued and unglued forms and the examples given of each in Chapter 3 are intended to stimulate further innovative design solutions that take full advantage of the potential of these new players in the market.

The final group of timber technologies examined differs from those above, in that their benefits are not primarily structural. Wood modification aims to introduce a quite radical transformation in the properties of the timber itself by the use of either thermal or chemical processing. The non-biocidal treatments employed are not especially new, but their commercial viability is a relatively recent phenomenon and can be attributed to a number of factors including a widespread need to find ways to make more use of less durable timber species in construction as well as stricter international regulation of imported tropical hardwoods. To date, these products remain insufficiently understood by designers and specifiers and their use in housing projects has also been limited by their premium pricing. Nevertheless, the range of uses in housing of materials produced via the thermal and chemical processes outlined in Chapter 4 is beginning to expand beyond the cladding and decking applications seen until now.

Each of the four chapters in this section includes several exemplar projects that have been selected to demonstrate the variety of ways in which the particular timber technology described has been used. With more experience comes greater confidence and, with it, a likely increase in design and construction innovation. Fully understanding the properties of the timber species, products and systems employed is fundamental to ensuring the experience gained is both positive and cumulative: Part 1 of this book provides an introduction to the uses and future potential of timber products and systems in UK housebuilding; Part 2 demonstrates the extraordinary range of applications in which they have been used so far.

Living Wall, Bury St. Edmunds (2008)
Studio MGM / Modece
Photographer: Matthew Smith

Chapter 1
The Green Timber House

No serious discussion of the timber building technologies we use today can avoid reference to their antecedents. The earliest of these—green timber construction—has been around since Neolithic times and continues in the UK to this day, where specialist companies still employ time-honoured housebuilding techniques to reuse and transform historical timber structures such as redundant barns, or to build entirely new homes that emulate the forms and carpentry skills evolved from traditional timber framing.

The ongoing development of these structures defined much of this country's domestic architecture from the Middle Ages through to the late 18th and early 19th centuries when the gravitation of large sections of the population away from the countryside into employment in the new, manufacturing towns and cities created an urgent need for mass housing that was largely serviced by the industrial manufacture of building materials, especially bricks. This, and the increasing difficulty in finding adequate supplies of good quality, domestically-grown hardwood timber led to a significant expansion in the use of imported pine and spruce (referred to collectively, at that time, as 'deal') from the Baltic countries, a trade that had begun as early as the 13th century but which, by the 18th century, had largely supplanted oak as the predominant species used in timber construction in the UK.

Whilst house building from hardwood timber in the UK did not entirely cease with the industrial revolution, its use thereafter was predominantly focused on the manufacture of windows, floorboards and doors rather than large section structural frames. This remained the case until relatively recently when an increasing number of architects and engineers began to review the merits of green timber construction and to reinterpret it for application in designs more visibly modern in conception than those previously associated with this technology. This shift in perception can largely be ascribed to increased concern for the environment and a desire to use renewable materials in their most basic form and, in doing so, to also benefit from the capacity of large section timber to sequester significant amounts of atmospheric carbon dioxide.

So, what does the term 'green timber construction' actually mean? Although green timber is also used for other building elements, such as external cladding, the term most frequently refers to the use of freshly cut (hard)woods in the creation of frames fabricated from large cross-section timbers; a craft tradition that dates back many centuries in England and Wales. Green timber has been employed by generations of carpenters in the construction of houses and barns and—more elaborately—in the roofs of churches and grand halls. Many outstanding examples of the use of this form of construction remain standing around the country, all bearing witness to the longevity of this method of building.

Frisealach, Roshven (2008)
Helen Lucas Architects
Photographer: Brendan MacNeill

Traditionally, oak was the pre-eminent timber for all purposes (although elm was also used in some parts of the country), with straight trunks milled to form the posts and beams of the building's frame. The thinner branches of the trees were used to make rafters and joists, the curved boughs provided braces and the saw sections used for floorboards. Any less good quality material was turned into laths and wattles: to all intents and purposes, no part of the tree was wasted. Nowadays, of course, most of the timber used in UK construction is kiln-dried; a process that is more difficult to carry out on large section material and which is generally considered to be unviable from an economic perspective due to the length of time taken in the kilning process and the amount of energy required.

Working with wood that is newly felled requires considerable carpentry skill and experience and is inevitably more intensive in terms of labour and time than other methods of timber construction. It would seem that this simple fact would preclude its inclusion in the range of timber technologies applied today, but, when used in conjunction with other systems, the handcraft skills involved are frequently complemented by more contemporary production methods. The bulk of new green timber houses built today are, in the main, traditional in appearance, due either to client preference or to planning requirements, but some excellent contemporary applications have emerged in recent years, particularly in rural areas where it is possible to source hardwood from broadleaf woodlands, or where site access issues render the delivery of larger panel systems more problematic. Whether traditional or modern, the key to the use of green timber is in understanding the mechanical properties of the different species commonly employed and how they can best be applied in this type of construction. Such knowledge is invariably provided by the carpenters who work in this field and whose experience and skills are of increasing value to architects and engineers wishing to meld the first principles of timber construction with modern design and fabrication technology.

To first understand how traditional methods and skills are being interpreted and applied today, there can be few better examples than the **Twilly Springs** house (2009-13), situated in the small village of West Hendred in Oxfordshire. Designed by Diamond Architects, the house is a hybrid of old and new green timber construction, the heart of the new dwelling being two 17th century cottages that were drastically altered and extended in the 1970s to form a much larger house. Although set within a Conservation Area and still containing part of the original elm-framed structure, the enlarged building was considered too far gone to merit listing and, on the advice of local historic timber specialists, Miles & Company, the house was demolished. In the course of doing so, the old frame was meticulously dismantled in order to repair it in workshop conditions and according to the Society for the Protection of Ancient Buildings (SPAB) rulebook. The ground floor posts of the historic frame were almost completely missing, whilst the ends of the floor beams had rotted away. These were replaced with new elm, using splayed and angled scarf joints to clasp the old and new wood tightly together. The convention in this type of operation is to replace decayed material with new pieces cut from the same species which, in this case, meant using timber seasoned to a moisture content of less than 10% to allow the ancient and the replacement timbers to move as one in response to structural loading and fluctuations in humidity. With English elm trees having been all but wiped out by Dutch elm disease, the necessary material was procured from Scotland.

The new build work was carried out in two phases, the first (2009-10) being to create a playroom annex, the second (2011-13) to build a new oak framed house incorporating the 17th century elm frame. The double-height playroom contains a minstrel gallery and has an exposed green oak structure, behind which is a lining of tongue and groove softwood. Graduated, lapped green oak external cladding completes an all-timber construction designed to recall the tradition of local barns. The building's seasoned oak windows and doors are located to suit the needs of the playroom, giving it an implicitly modern appearance yet also (on completion of the new house and a connecting link) the impression that it is a later addition to an older dwelling.

Twilly Springs House, West Hendred, nr. Wantage, Oxfordshire (2009-13)
Diamond Architects
Photographer: David Grandorge

As with the playroom, the replacement house has a traditional frame of newly harvested green oak, a technology that requires highly disciplined co-ordination between the design, fabrication and construction members of the project team. This is because green oak, like all timbers, is a variable material that shrinks and distorts: in the case of oak this process happens slowly as it becomes seasoned with age and the whole method of construction—essentially one of prefabrication—is based upon this capacity of the wood to shrink. The fabrication sequence is to first cut a combination of dovetail, mortice and tenon and scarf joints into the posts, beams and curved diagonal braces and to then assemble the whole before the natural shrinkage becomes too advanced. The structure gradually settles, with the joints (some with wooden pegs) becoming tighter as the timber slowly dries. In the case of the Twilly Springs house, however, delays to the programme meant that material shrinkage and distortion required joints to be slightly enlarged at the time of assembly.

The second technical challenge inherent in this type of construction is how to integrate seasoned (and thus stable) timber components, such as doors, windows, staircase and floorboards, into a frame that is still in the process of shrinking—a problem overcome by rebating these elements into the green oak structure, thus enabling them to move independently. Modern regulations too, impact upon the wall build-up around green timber frames: demanding requirements for energy performance and weather protection make it difficult to expose the frame externally as there is a danger of cold bridging and possible interstitial condensation. A pragmatic approach that combined external insulation and an outer skin of render was therefore taken, with only the jettied frame over the entrance giving any indication of the house's green timber credentials. Finally, hardwood frames are highly susceptible to moisture during assembly and rain will introduce swelling and possible unsightly staining; problems avoided here by enclosing the emerging house in a huge scaffolded canopy during a year of construction.

Once inside the house, the impact is dramatic: the staircase rises within a mathematically precise three-storey grid of green oak and plaster that has been conceived as a dialogue between the repaired elm frame and the new oak structure, each of which is clearly expressed and where every connection detail has been beautifully articulated. Although deliberately in the tradition of the medieval great hall, this refined space at the heart of the Twilly Springs House could never be described as pastiche: the building's carefully developed structure of green elm and oak is not only a successful hybrid of old and new timbers, it also an impressive combination of ancient and modern design and construction knowledge and skills.

Twilly Springs House,
West Hendred, nr. Wantage, Oxfordshire (2009-13)
Diamond Architects
Photographer: David Grandorge

**Newstead, Bottom Lane,
Seer Green, Buckinghamshire**
(2010)
Baca Architects
Photographer: Alastair Lever

Newstead (2010) in the Buckinghamshire hamlet of Seer Green, by Baca Architects, might be considered to be at the opposite end of the green timber construction spectrum from the Twilly Springs House, its external form unashamedly modernist in conception. Its materials are less obviously so, however, until antecedents such as the early US East Coast work of architects, e.g. Charles Gwathmey, is taken into consideration. Gwathmey and his partner Robert Siegel, along with others in the group referred to as the New York Five, took the tenets of modernist architecture and combined them with the balloon frame method of timber construction common in US housebuilding in the 1960s. The Platonic forms of the houses by Gwathmey Siegel were easily distinguished from those of peers such as Richard Meier by not being painted white in homage to the earlier European houses of, in particular, Le Corbusier, but were instead clad in uncoated cedar and thus very visibly formed from timber. At the time, the material honesty of the practice's use of wood was revelatory to many architects and the influence of this approach can still be seen today in modern houses throughout north America and beyond.

Newstead then, whilst unusual in design and form—at least in this part of the Chilterns—can thus be regarded as part of a century-old architectural lineage that spans two continents and which, in recent years, has had evident influence on the design of a considerable proportion of modern, bespoke timber housing in the UK. The main structure of the house is comprised of a super-insulated timber frame although, unlike its American counterpart, the system used here is of the platform variety (see Chapter 2), the standard solution in most UK timber-based housebuilding. That said, its conventional application is in simpler configurations where timescale and material economies are the primary drivers. Here, the building's layout has been developed in response to site considerations, the five-bedroom eco-home being set into a steep slope and entered at first floor level, where window bays set into facets in the curved plan of the living area provide a range of views towards the distant hills. This upper floor sits under a barrel vaulted green roof designed not only to slowly mature and provide new habitat, but also to reduce rainwater run-off rates as part of the house's sophisticated eco strategy.

It is, however, Newstead's green oak cladding that is its most defining feature; a combination of long, narrow vertical boards, projecting cills and lintels around window openings and deep, large-section open screens providing solar shading and privacy to larger window areas. When freshly cut, green oak cladding can range in colour from pink to a pale honey hue, deepening to a golden yellow after the surface of the sawn wood has dried, before eventually weathering to a natural silver. The choice of this species for Newstead's cladding is therefore entirely apposite: highly durable, the steadily mellowing green oak ties the building to its woody surroundings whilst demonstrating its virtues as a material well suited to the imperatives of modern design and construction.

At the other end of the country, the climatic conditions and remoteness of the site at Roshven, on the edge of Loch Ailort (an Argyll sea loch), largely determined the primary material choices for **Frisealach** ("The Fraser's Place", 2008) , designed by Helen Lucas Architects for her family and husband/client, fellow architect Malcolm Fraser. The house is located just a few miles off the historic A830. The route is better known as The Road to the Isles and links Fort William with the fishing port of Mallaig, a ferry point for the Isle of Skye. The scenic rail route that also connects these two towns via the Glenfinnan Viaduct is perhaps more familiar to younger travellers as the Hogwarts Railway.

Frisealach has spectacular views to the islands of Eigg and Rhum and to the Arisaig peninsula to the north, but the site's location on Inverness-shire's west coast also means that weather conditions there can often be harsh. This, allied to the fact that the challenges of access to the eight-metre-wide and 20-metre-long site precluded the use of the standard timber construction solutions used in Scotland, whether frame or panel (see Chapter 2), indicated a more site-responsive approach was required.

Planning permission had originally been granted (to previous owners of the land) for a building on another part of the site but, this being a low-lying and overshadowed boggy piece of ground, would have involved felling a huge number of trees and so a new application was made

Frisealach, Roshven (2008)
Helen Lucas Architects
Photographer: Brendan MacNeill

to position the house some eight metres above the rugged coastline, between a rock outcrop and a lively burn (stream). In this location, the only really viable choice for the structure was a pre-cut, large-section timber frame, elevated on 14 green oak posts bolted to concrete pads, eschewing any need to level the ground but also giving the impression of a house floating over the rocks. The site having dictated a long and narrow plan (the house is one room plus a corridor wide), the post and beam solution, fabricated by Carpenter Oak and Woodland, uses green oak (from France) where the two-storey frame and monopitch roof is exposed externally and uncoated Douglas fir (from England) for the internal structural elements.

Inside, the walls and ceilings are lined with fire-treated and lime-washed tongue-and-groove softwood panelling; the flooring throughout is oak. Externally, the four-bedroom dwelling is clad horizontally with green oak boards, the material's high durability an important factor in the house's ability to resist strong north-westerly winds coming in off the sea and, in combination with 200mm of hemp and cotton insulation in the walls, in keeping the interior warm and draught free. Indeed, Frisealach is extremely energy efficient, heated mainly by a wood-burning stove that sits centrally to the open plan dining and living area. The floor to ceiling windows in the double height space lock perpendicularly to avoid the need for a corner post so that, when open, the view is uninterrupted, with little division between the room interior and the external deck that runs around the house's north and west elevations. Settled on its rocky plinth and away from the water's edge, Frisealach appears at one with its natural surroundings

Taigh na Coille, Loch Ailort (2012)
Helen Lucas Architects
Photographer: Angus Bremner

16

and the extremes of weather that have conditioned its orientation and form. Likewise, the courageous decision to use green timber as the house's primary construction material (the architects hadn't previously worked with it) was an important contributor to the development of the design, resulting in an exemplary project in a spectacular location.

Building a house for personal use can sometimes result in it becoming "a shop window" for its architect and may, on rare occasions, lead to a new commission. Despite its remoteness, such proved to be the case with Frisealach and for a neighbouring site with similar topographic features. In the case of **Taigh na Coille** ("House of the Woods", 2012), also by Helen Lucas Architects, the land in question offered a slightly different panorama: still with prospects to Eigg and Rhum, the key determinant for the client was the view to Eilean nan Gobhar (Goat Island), conjuring up as it did, memories of childhood summer holidays camping on the beach at Roshven and the occasional rowing boat trip over to the rocky, cliff-girthed islet. Having found the site and admired the neighbouring house, it made sense to employ its architect and to benefit from her prior experience of construction in a place with complex access and foundation issues. Unlike Frisealach, however, the house is designed to sit low in the rocky landscape, back from the water's edge and sheltered to its rear from the prevailing south-westerly wind by a stand of Scots pines that channels the route to its entrance.

A larger house on a wider site than its neighbour, Taigh na Coille has a T-shaped plan, the entrance is located at one end of the long, double height volume that, on its lower level, accommodates the kitchen, dining and living area, the latter looking out over the rocky shore, whilst above is a home office/study and a TV room. Perpendicular to this, the single storey bedroom wing is oriented to ensure all its rooms have views across the water, with the master bedroom specifically aligned with Goat Island. In structural form and materials, the house is similar to Frisealach, the external elements being a green oak external frame, the internal ones of Douglas fir with, once again, the Carpenter Oak and Woodland team bringing their considerable expertise to bear on the construction. Only the house's external faces and the thermal insulation differ: instead of green oak, horizontal Siberian larch cladding boards have been used (except between window panels where the same material is installed vertically); and wood fibre insulation (Pavatex) has replaced the hemp and cotton of the predecessor house.

As with its neighbour, Taigh na Coille appears to hover on an understructure of sturdy green oak posts connected to concrete pads that are set on the rocks so as to cause as little disturbance to the natural landscape as possible. The master bedroom and the living area have their own external timber decks, with stairs down to the rocks below. Overall, this is an architecture of understatement: deferential to its context, its construction providing a robust barrier to the extremes of weather regularly encountered in Scotland's rugged north-west: a quintessentially modern green timber house in which structural form has very definitely followed function.

Six hundred miles south, the exploration of the contemporary potential of green timber construction could not be carried out more differently. The 350 acre (142 hectares) working forest at Hooke Park near Beaminster in Dorset being home to a hotbed of research and development undertaken by students of the Architectural Association (AA), the owner and operator of the estate. The Hooke Park campus represents a 30-year history of experimental timber construction and rural architecture, with the past 10 years in particular seeing the emergence of an extraordinary range of green timber buildings within the forest that have been designed and constructed by Masters degree students using advanced computing methods and robot fabrication technology. In 2009-10, the school's Intermediate Unit 2 produced a schematic design for a caretaker's house on the site, a project that the AA subsequently commissioned Pier's Taylor's Invisible Studio to develop into a prototypical low-cost exemplar building using only timber grown and felled within the forest and in its green state. The **Caretaker's House**

**Caretaker's House,
Hooke Park, Dorset** (2012)
Invisible Studio with AA
Intermediate Unit 2
Photographer: Valerie Bennett

(2012) thus utilises unseasoned cedar, Douglas fir, larch, poplar and spruce as appropriate, with wood sources also providing fuel to heat the building and for its insulation material. The only non-timber structural elements employed in the project are the steel mini-pile foundations.

The three-bedroom house has a continuous, undulating roof supported on a primary structure of large section Douglas fir posts, its unusual sectional profile generated by, at the house's east end, the wish to gain maximum sunlight penetration into the master bedroom and, at its western end, a first floor living space designed to provide a high-level observation position from which the extent of the campus can be surveyed. The bedroom block is separated from the house's living areas by what the architect describes as a 'dog trot'—a term common throughout the Southeastern United States during the 19th and early 20th centuries for a covered passageway between two parts of a building and which, when the sliding, timber-clad door on the north face of the Caretaker's House is open, frames the views into the forest.

The plan of the Caretaker's House is organised according to cardinal points: its 'heavy' north wall containing few openings and its 150m deep softwood studs packed with Pavatex wood fibre insulation material, while the south faces of the bedrooms and living areas open to a verandah that runs the length of the building to provide an extension to the living space. Internally the house is lined throughout with fair-faced plywood sheets.

Perhaps the most obviously experimental and visually apparent feature of the house is found in the design and fabrication of its external cladding. Specified to be of either Douglas fir or larch, the rough-sawn boards employed, in the sections of the building that either recess (e.g. in the 'dog-trot') or rise at angles where the roof steps up, are cut from wide boards so as to taper to quite narrow dimensions at their other end. As installed, narrow horizontal cladding boards on the walls meet the narrow end of tapered planks that, broader at their other end, fan upwards to adjoin a plane of wide horizontal cladding boards. Creating a precision-cut geometrical tour-de-force of this sort with unseasoned timber is something of a triumph, delivering to the house an illusory optical effect of perspectival depth.

The Caretaker's House is undoubtedly unusual in that its conception and low-budget realisation have been undertaken within an ongoing research and development programme that not only explores ways in which advanced design and fabrication technology can impact on green timber construction methods, but which also actively encourages experimentation and innovation intended to push the boundaries of what is conventionally termed as 'sustainable timber construction'. The lessons from Hooke Park could well open new doors for green timber construction and, whilst the Architectural Association may deliver only a relatively small cadre of specialists in advanced timber design into the architectural profession each year, these people will, in due course form their own practices and disseminate their hard-won knowledge to others.

Whilst the bulk of new timber housing is now manufactured offsite, the technology involved is unlikely to be able to answer all of the challenges inherent in the UK's current housing crisis. With its ever-increasing band of champions, green timber construction could have an important role to play in dealing with affordable housing shortages in remoter parts of the country, creating opportunities for skills training and employment in forestry, carpentry and construction and thus contributing to local economies and sustaining rural communities. Development and support for the green timber construction sector can play an important role in raising the value of the UK forest resource, with the consequent benefit, in small part, of helping to reduce the amount—and cost—of imported timber: savings that can be redirected to investment in new forest planting. Application of Circular Economy philosophy in this way may be small, but it is also incremental: maximising the use of indigenous materials, as in the Caretaker's House, demonstrates what can be achieved in new residential design when imagination, technical knowledge, manufacturing skill—and green timber—are brought into combination.

**Caretaker's House,
Hooke Park, Dorset** (2012)
Invisible Studio with AA
Intermediate Unit 2
Photographer: Valerie Bennett

Chapter 2

The Framed and Panelled Timber House

Strange as it may seem, the evolution of the modern timber frame can be attributed less to increases in the general understanding of timber properties, than to improvements in mechanical sawmilling and the beginning of mass production of metal nails in 1830s America. These technological advances led to the development of two new timber-framing methods: the Balloon Frame and the Platform Timber Frame. These systems are easily distinguished by the fact that the posts (or studs) of the former run vertically for more than one storey whilst the latter has single-storey high posts (studs) with each storey being built separately, the lower wall serving as the platform (and working floor) to support the next level of wall structure. Originally, Balloon Frame buildings were two-storeys high, with the vertical members running unbroken over the height of the building, from the ground cill or plate to the head plate that supported the roof rafters. Horizontal wall plates fixed to the vertical members supported the intermediate floor joists. Most importantly, however, the developments in sawmilling and nail production mentioned above facilitated the evolution of lighter weight frames (requiring material from fewer trees to form the structure of a house) and the possibility that a single individual could erect a complete house using only a hammer and a saw.

Onsite frame construction in this way has, however, largely been transcended in the UK by the prefabrication of frames in controlled factory conditions. Unlike in North America, where the Balloon Frame is still the pre-eminent system in use today, the Platform Timber Frame has become the dominant method in the UK, its attributes being more suited to climatic variability and offsite manufacturing. It is the system of choice in Scotland for more than 75% of new residential projects, whilst its use in England and Wales has continued to increase in recent years (and now has around 20% market share) in response to regulatory changes driven by concerns for the environment and the need to reduce energy usage. These regional variations disguise the actual number of homes built using this method since the overall percentages relate to markets of different size, with Scotland currently producing around 15,000 houses per annum and England and Wales delivering around twice as many timber frame units.

Continuing shortages of skilled construction site personnel coupled with political demands for ever increasing numbers of new-build homes have also contributed to the ongoing expansion of this tried and tested technology. Manufactured in offsite factory conditions, timber frame offers greatly improved precision in house construction, can accommodate increased levels of insulation and offer high levels of airtightness. Importantly, by getting the walls and roof assembled quickly, it allows follow-on trades to continue working in a weather-protected environment. The time savings available from using timber frame construction in open-panel format can be significant, often being as much as 30% quicker than with more traditional building methods and thus delivering commensurate reductions in cost. Savings in both of these areas can be further increased if doors, windows, insulation and other elements are

Woodpeckers,
New Forest (2015)
Ström Architects
Photographer: Luke Hayes

23

installed at the factory stage (timber frame closed-panel), with far less wastage and significantly lower transportation impact than would occur with standard on-site construction processes. All of these points contribute to timber frame's impressive sustainability credentials, criteria that form an important part of the UK Government's 2025 Industrial Strategy.

Platform timber frame technology is also flexible in that it is equally applicable in use in urban, suburban and rural situations and across a wide range of building types. Because the frame is often concealed behind non-wood exterior or interior finishes, however, general awareness that a house's structure may be predominantly of timber remains low. Yet this is one of the most efficient methods of construction employed in the UK today, due to its ease of use and its ability to deliver excellent energy performance and 'whole life costs'.

The Stick-Built Timber Frame

Returning to the first principles of modern timber frame construction (the idea of the solo worker with a hammer and saw), fabrication that takes place entirely on-site is often referred to as 'stick-built' and, whilst it is slower, more labour intensive and, inevitably, can be less precise than frames that are manufactured offsite, the method nevertheless still has an important role to play in the timber frame housing sector wherever circumstances demand. A good example is **Woodpeckers** (2015) by Ström Architects, a two-storey replacement for a 1930s bungalow situated amongst fields and private woodland just outside of the New Forest National Park. Planning constraints meant there could be no more than a 30% increase in the house's footprint size over that of its predecessor, a figure that included all overhangs. In response, the architects maximised the allowable area to 195 sq/m in two ways: first, by eschewing the use of extended eaves to the roof, lest they be included in the area calculation and, second, with a slab-sided solution in which the house's glazing has been fixed flush with the exterior of the building envelope. Paradoxically, provision for a 20 sq/m conservatory was included within the total allowable area, valuable additional square metres that, rather than being built on to the house in the ubiquitous, lean-to manner, has been cleverly integrated into its overall form as a single-storey, almost flat-roofed element, that extends seamlessly from the main open plan space.

Despite this extremely efficient planning, the tight budget available was unlikely to match client ambitions on size of spaces and quality of finishes and, to avoid compromise, efficiencies needed to be made in the building fabric and structure. With a desire also to have full height openings to create a strong internal-external relationship—openings that, with a traditional masonry construction would have required large amounts of steel with proportionately larger costs—the architects elected for the simplicity of a single structural system: a timber frame superstructure stick-built onsite above a piled concrete slab, with the studwork filled and over-clad with insulation to create a thermally- and structurally-efficient envelope. The same economic logic was applied to the house's construction in the setting out of its width and in its roof design, the dimensions for which were established by the performance restrictions of standard timber truss components. Similar pragmatism is evident in the house's fenestration where the position and size of the openings have been generated by floor-to-ceiling gaps in the timber facade. Clad overall with untreated, vertically-fixed Siberian larch boards, their gradually-weathering colour contrasts well with the white-painted masonry chimney that marks the transition between the living and conservatory areas.

A very different reason for embracing a stick-built timber frame approach is to be found four hundred or so miles north in the Scottish Borders where the stone-built shell of a former mill building has been transformed into a comfortable, modern home. The former grain threshing mill is part of the Southside Steading, a collection of disused farm buildings that nestle into an exposed hillside overlooking a valley near the Royal Burgh of Peebles. The footprint of the steading's derelict farmhouse was adjudged to be too small for the new family house

Woodpeckers, New Forest (2015)
Ström Architects
Photographer: Luke Hayes

required, resulting in the adjacent mill building being selected for conversion. The client's brief to WT Architecture for **The Mill** (2014) asked for open plan living spaces to be designed in such way as to allow different gathering areas, with smaller, more cellular bedrooms fitted into the building's extended plan.

With its roof and interior structure beyond repair, the building was stripped back to its shell condition before using stones from the site to repair the walls. Repointing with lime mortar completed this task and, with the envelope finally stabilised and capped, an independent timber frame was constructed within, the existing stone walls being used to brace the stick-built structure. The cavity separating the two wall elements is fully insulated, as is the frame itself, a solution only made possible with an on-site construction method that was able to address the inevitable variation in width between the old and the new. The upper, timber-clad walls to the long elevations have been designed to rise behind and above the stone parapet to support the roof, whilst a clerestory window has been inserted behind the narrow gap created between the roof and the top of the gable end wall: a neat detail that also clearly distinguishes the modern intervention from the original structure. Other windows in the black-painted, larch-clad 'attic' walls that appear above the parapets to the long elevations have been designed, where possible, to align with openings in the existing stone walls.

The Mill, Southside Steading, Scottish Borders (2014)
WT Architecture
Photographer: Andrew Lee

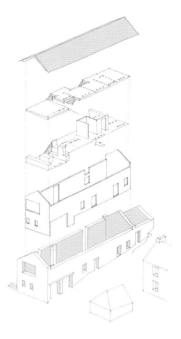

Ott's Yard, Tufnell Park, North London (2014)
VPPR Architects
Photographers:
Tatiana von Preussen (top)
Hélène Binet (bottom)

Internally, the house is simply and economically lined with panels of unpainted spruce plywood, a homogeneous solution that links the various split-levels implanted into the long section of the building to take advantage of the site's steep incline. With the plan arranged around the central 'hub dining area, two separate staircases lead off from this space: that towards the south steps either down to the kitchen or up to the main living area whilst, in the opposite corner, a long stair leads up to two of the house's three bedrooms, with the third, on a half level, accessed via a short stair from the living room itself. This, seemingly complex, spatial arrangement has minimised the area within the Mill House given over to corridors and has delivered the different gathering spaces specified in the original brief. A box within a box and a complete reversal of the norm: the Mill is now a modern, lightweight timber house sheltered within an old stone structure that now functions, in the manner of Scotland's castle architecture, as a thick curtain wall.

Building within one set of existing walls can be challenging enough but, faced with 23 Party Walls, the normal natural instinct might be to stay well clear of any attempt to develop a site likely to be fraught with myriad legal obstacles. **Ott's Yard** (2014), is tucked away in Tufnell Park, an area of North London that bridges the border between the Boroughs of Camden and Islington. The plot is bounded on all three sides of its awkward triangular configuration by the rear gardens of the aforementioned 23, mostly terraced, properties. Once the location of a joinery workshop, the site is completely hidden from view, with only a long, narrow access strip between it and Southcote Road. Undeterred, architects vPPR conceived an ingenious design for a pair of two-bedroom houses and gardens that completely fills the sloping, 60/30° set-square-shaped plot, with an access courtyard squeezed in between the two. Needless to say, the plan form is complicated, made no less so by being based upon an abstraction of the site's geometry that has the courtyard at the centre of a pin-wheel, fractal pattern and which is the pivotal point for the layout of the two houses.

The construction was no less challenging; with only a narrow access passage to the site available, the use of a prefabricated panel system was impracticable and so the homes have had their timber frames stick-built on site. Heavily insulated with Kingspan's Kooltherm product, the external walls—in response to neighbours' wishes—are clad in brickwork similar to that of the surrounding buildings' rear elevations. With no possibility to locate windows in the boundary walls of the two houses, only the facades that look onto the internal courtyard carry fenestration. Large, triangular rooflights set into the, no-less-complex, sedum-covered roof planes bring light into the homes from above, delivering a lofty, open feel to the double-height central spaces. Steel beams have been used to support these rooflights, with plywood sheets glued and screwed to the timber frames to form stressed skin panels. The fractal geometries that generated the design concept are further reflected in the setting out of the timber floorboards, the triangular ceramic tiles used on floors and walls and in the layout of the external brick paviors and garden planters.

Given the two houses' complexity of form and construction, it is astonishing that their cost on completion came within the set budget of £650,000. One of the homes was recently on sale for around twice that sum, indicating—perhaps more than the well-recognised excesses of house-price inflation in the capital—that the flexibility and lighter-weight benefits of on-site timber frame fabrication can help to make this method of construction economically advantageous even in the delivery of highly original dwellings on tightly constrained urban sites.

Difficulties with site access also made onsite frame fabrication the optimal solution to the challenging problem of constructing a replacement house in an active landslip zone on the clifftops of Dorset's Jurassic coastline near Lyme Regis. Unlike the previous example, however, the timber form of the **Crow's Nest** (2016) by Winchester-based architects, AR Design Studio, is entirely visible. The clients had actually intended to extend their holiday home but, despite it being some distance from the sea edge, the site moved in the course of one night during

the unprecedented torrential rain experienced during the early months of 2014, causing the existing house to break in two. Building a new house on the same site, therefore required a structural solution designed to prevent future failure. Working closely with engineers Eckersley O'Callaghan, the architects conceived the Crow's Nest as a timber-framed house planted on top of a complex foundation arrangement. Detailed geological surveys had indicated that layers of Silty Sand and Upper Greensand Head would need to be pushed through in order to reach the Foxmould Sand layer far below. Using reinforced concrete piles topped with a grillage of ground beams, foundations were constructed that allow the house to sit lightly on the plot whilst offering the necessary support in the event of further landscape-induced movement.

Dwarf walls were then built on this concrete base structure, onto which a structural steel frame was laid as an adjustable raft. Mechanical jacks, positioned in strategic locations beneath this frame, allow the house to be securely re-levelled, should circumstances so demand. With these, far from standard, foundations in place, it was initially thought the house's different pod elements could be delivered as completed modules, but difficulties in accessing the site resulted instead in a lightweight timber frame being built in-situ, with additional, isolated steel elements located in this superstructure to make the house's large open plan spaces, asymmetrical roof profiles and the framing of its sliding doors technically possible.

Perhaps taking inspiration from the cleaving apart of its predecessor, the 180 sq/m house has been designed to have a traditional cabin-like-form that appears to have been split, twisted and rotated to create four engaged pod structures. The Siberian larch-clad pods are offset from each other and face slightly different directions, emphasising the intention that their irregular forms should appear to have tectonically shifted away from each other. The rough-sawn, vertically-fixed rainscreen cladding extends over the roofs, with each ridge-line laid to a slightly different angle and the boards themselves installed in random widths.

The Crow's Nest is a house the architects, engineers and clients appear to have taken considerable mutual delight in resolving its multiple technical complexities: indeed, the simplest aspect of the whole exercise would seem to be the onsite fabrication of its timber frame: an eminently practical design choice that has made its own significant contribution to the formation of the house's remarkable forms.

Some 225 miles apart, the landscapes of West Dorset and Dungeness in Kent are entirely different, the former being a UNESCO World Heritage Site boasting an almost continuous sequence of rock formations covering the Triassic, Jurassic and Cretaceous periods, whilst the latter headland is mostly comprised of a rather bleak beach that, nevertheless, is reputed to be one of the largest expanses of shingle in Europe. Home to some 600 plant species, Dungeness is the only place in the UK officially classified as a desert and its unique environment is recognised and protected by a plethora of conservation designations.

It has two other notable features: it lies within spitting distance of the Dungeness B nuclear power station; and it is the location for some of the most remarkable timber houses to have been built in the UK in recent years. True, in architectural terms, a few of these might be regarded as idiosyncratic, but the best of them can be said to represent highly creative reinterpretations of the traditional timber-based, black bitumen-coated fishing cottages and huts that previously stood on these sites and examples of which still abound amongst the detritus of ex-railway carriages and caravans that populate this seemingly unplanned landscape. Not that there is a total absence of planning conditions here—Shepway District Council will permit reinvention of this highly unusual local vernacular with the proviso that any new proposals keep to the footprints, roof pitches and ridgelines of the structures they are replacing. A number of exemplary projects have emerged in recent years in response to these simple constraints including, within this veritable timber architecture expo, Simon Conder Associates's Black Rubber Beach House and El Ray (the latter featuring in Chapter 7—The Remodelled Timber House), NORD Architecture's Shingle House, Guy Hollaway Architects' Pobble House and **North Vat** (2014), by Rodic Davidson Architects.

This last example is made up of three adjoining pavilions, each with gabled profiles and rough-sawn larch-clad walls. Whilst giving a respectful nod to the bitumen-coated walls of its predecessor on the site, the house deliberately breaks away from conventional form and layout with its main, two-storey block (containing the living/kitchen/dining space on the ground floor and the master bedroom above) linked by an L-shaped, fully-glazed entrance hallway to two

North Vat, Dungeness (2014)
Rodic Davidson Architects
Photographer: Hélène Binet

smaller cabins (one a study; the other a second bedroom). The roofs and walls of the three new elements have, however, as their first layer of defence against the ravages of the elements on this exposed site, an open-jointed rainscreen of black-stained larch cladding boards, each of which is 80mm wide and meticulously-fixed at 88mm centres. All of the house's openings and junctions (windows, rooflights and doors) are similarly set out on this 88mm module to ensure there is no interruption to the continuous rhythm of the cladding. Indeed, the quality of joinery (by Folkestone-based sustainable construction and passivhaus specialists, Eco-Librium Solutions Ltd) throughout is outstanding: in the careful chamfering of the board ends that meet the minimal window frames; in the fitting of the rooflights to lie flush with the surface of the rainscreen; and in the repetitively-accurate angle cuts to the ends of the vertical and sloping boards where they meet at the junction between wall and roof.

Behind the ultra-refined detail visible is an equally sophisticated, but necessarily robust, answer to the waterproofing of the three structures and, beneath this membrane layer, timber frames that were stick-built on-site. In this case, the frames were modelled on computer before the individual 'sticks' were machine-cut to precise dimensions in the contractor's offsite facility. Once delivered to site, the assembly team could proceed to build in the confident knowledge that the separate elements would accurately combine. Had it not been possible to deliver this high level of construction accuracy, it is very unlikely that either a reliably watertight solution or the beautifully executed rainscreen would have been achievable with on-site stick-built fabrication. North Vat may be a small project but, in the precision manufacture and assembly of its stick-built timber framing lies a textbook example of the very high quality results that can be achieved using more advanced versions of this particular technology.

North Vat, Dungeness (2014)
Rodic Davidson Architects
Photographer: Hélène Binet

**The Sett, Totland,
Isle of Wight** (2014)

Dow Jones Architects

Photographer: David Grandorge

The Timber Frame Open-Panel House

Timber frame open-panel systems are structural engineered elements designed to form the inside load-bearing leaf of external walls. The studs and rails of the frame are made from 90, 140 or 235 mm CLS* treated softwood, over which a structural sheet (sheathing) of either 9 mm WBP Ply or OSB** board is fixed to its outer face, after which a vapour-permeable but waterproof (breather) membrane is tacked on. The panels are delivered without insulation or vapour control layers and with the inner face of the frame still open, hence the name. Once the building has been made weathertight and the electrical and plumbing carcassing completed, insulation can be inserted between the studs/rails and a vapour-proof barrier tacked on before the panel's internal Ply or OSB lining is fixed in place. Depending upon the particular system employed, U-values ranging from 0.26 down to 0.15 W per sq/m K, can be achieved.

Developer house styles, local market preferences or planning requirements generally result in outer wall leaves built using brick, block/render, stone, or timber. Increasingly, however, external masonry leafs are being dispensed with in favour of 'single-skin' cladding systems, i.e. render or timber board systems that are fixed to battens on the outside face of the panelled wall. The combination, for example, of an open-panel load-bearing frame structure with external timber cladding is significantly lighter in weight than a traditional brick and block cavity wall and can be built on smaller foundations. It can also, if pushed to the edge of the allowable footprint, result in larger internal room dimensions. The assembly speed and accuracy of this construction method have also proved important factors in the popularity of this form of construction.

Each of these considerations is recognisable in the decision to use this system to build a holiday retreat for a family of four at Totland on the Isle of Wight. Totland itself was developed in the late 19th century as a residential and seaside resort and **The Sett** (2014) has been neatly inserted by Dow Jones Architects into the former orchard of a large house built in the early 1920s. Designing a house around and between existing trees is rarely straightforward, but the Sett takes full advantage of its location. Sited at the eastern end of the orchard, the house is reached along a small lane that leads between tall trees to a small entrance courtyard in

front of its two-storey, north elevation. The position of the fruit trees has largely determined the layout of the four-bedroom house, with its plan arranged around an inner courtyard that is itself centred on an apple tree. The ground floor has been orchestrated to create a range of vistas, the main one being the clear line of sight from the entrance hall, through the apple tree courtyard, to the extensive rear garden beyond. Other, diagonal, views connect the ground floor spaces and, with light seeming to appear around corners, give the impression that the house is far bigger than its actual floor area.

The subtleties of the Sett's planning do not stop there: the ground floor rooms also take advantage of the sun's journey through the day: the kitchen faces to the east to catch the morning light; the living room gains light through the day via its south-facing aspect; whilst the dining room looks out to the west and the evening sun. A brick chimney forms the vertical axis around which the lower part of the house is centred. With each of these areas having a different size, shape and orientation as well as the aforementioned visual interconnections with other spaces, some structural rigour has been necessary to ensure coherence and economy in the house's construction. Planned, therefore, on a simple grid, the Sett has been built using a prefabricated, platform timber frame open-panel system, a logical solution for a design that required to be accurately set out on site. To the north and east, the upper floor is jettied out to create an L-shaped arcade below, the outside edge of which is defined by a series of large-section timber posts; a similarly-supported projecting roof over the single-storey living/dining area provides a sheltered terrace. Unifying the house's cuboidal forms is its outer skin of Siberian larch boards, vertically-fixed and butted together, with their lengths corresponding to storey heights. The ends of the cladding boards to the upper floor lap over those fixed to the lower wall, a proportioning technique that fulfils two additional functions: it emphasises the layering and thickness of the boards' and, more practically, it avoids the need to use joined pieces of timber.

The homogeneity of the Sett's outer skin is further underlined by its thick, black, bituminous paint coating, a technique used traditionally in this area to protect the hulls of boats and which, in this instance, similarly seals the timber surface whilst still allowing the grain of the material to show through. The architects' other reason for applying this continuous colour to the surface of the yellow-green Siberian larch cladding and the reddish-brown Sapele hardwood window frames can be attributed to a desire for the house's formal qualities to dominate, with the black contrasting strongly with the Douglas fir joinery of the interiors. The crisp composition of the Sett is a measure of the quality that can be achieved with timber frame open-panel construction: further examples are to found throughout Part Two of this book.

**The Sett, Totland,
Isle of Wight** (2014)
Dow Jones Architects
Photographer: David Grandorge

The Timber Frame Closed-Panel House

As with open-panel timber frames, closed-panel systems are prefabricated in clean, dry workshop environments.. The manufacturing process is similar: structural engineered frames are constructed using treated softwood timber studs and rails, onto the outer face of which a structural sheet material of either 9 mm Plywood or OSB** is fixed. At this stage in the manufacturing process, a breather membrane is fixed to the outer face of the panel. Insulation is then fitted between the studs and a vapour barrier tacked over this before sheathing is fixed to the inner face of the frame. The insulation & vapour control layers can be specified to meet particular thermal performance requirements, hence the 90, 140 or 235 mm CLS* stud options that are generally available from closed-panel manufacturers. Increasingly, doors and windows are pre-fitted into the panels at the factory stage, the advantage being greater ease and speed in obtaining a thermally-efficient, airtight structure once the panels are on site. with U-values from 0.25 down to 0.10 W per sq/m K possible. Service battens are also often applied to the internal sheathing within the workshop to provide a service void for the mechanical and electrical services, again with on-site work reduced to a minimum.

The Cinque Ports town of Rye in East Sussex is only 14 miles west of Dungeness in Kent, but architecturally it could hardly be more different. In its centre, cobbled lanes like Mermaid Street are lined with medieval, half-timbered houses and remains of the town walls built in this period can still be found on the **Cinque Ports Street** (2015) site of the mixed-use residential development by JD Architects. Despite its former industrial use, the development lies close to the historic riverfront shipyard and the characteristics of its architecture are evoked in the timber-cladding of the four-storey elevation of its main block. At first sight, this street-facing apartment building appears simple, an impression entirely belied by the complexity of piled foundations that required to be sleeved and cased to depths of 10-18 metres to avoid disturbing the medieval moat immediately underneath and from which water still flows below ground. The piles and service runs are therefore positioned to avoid this and other subterranean archaeological features, with the utilities designed to pass through deeper parts of the town wall that are either damaged or missing.

Given the site conditions, the architects have, remarkably, managed to fit two shop units, a vehicle entrance to an inner courtyard plus two car spaces into the building's ground level, with six apartments and two penthouse units on the three floors above. The courtyard itself contains a detached house and a studio unit above seven more covered parking spaces. Remnants of the town wall align with the rear of the apartment building but, stopping just short of it, continues, as a presence, in outline in the courtyard paving. Memory plays its part, too, in the development's above ground construction, where a timber frame closed-panel system and floor cassettes have brought the town's timber architecture traditions into the 21st century. More practically, the selection of the construction method was influenced by the constrained nature of the site and its location next to a busy road junction. These conditions called for quick offloading of deliveries and fast, accurate construction, criteria met by the closed-panel system being able to quickly provide an airtight and thermally efficient building envelope. The development's sustainability bona fides are more visibly apparent in the rainscreen cladding to the street: not only are its vertically-fixed Kebony® boards spaced 8mm apart to ensure effective ventilation, but southern yellow pine used in chemically-modified form (more detail about which can be found in Chapter Four—The Modified Timber House) is also highly durable in saltwater conditions (it is frequently used for ships' decking) and unlikely, therefore, to be much affected by the sea breezes blowing through the town of Rye.

Cinque Ports Street is an unusual but entirely appropriate application of timber frame closed-panel systems: other outstanding examples punctuate the chapters in Part Two and are indicative of their widespread use in housing projects throughout the UK.

Cinque Ports Street, Rye (2015)
JD Architects
Photographer: Oliver Perrott

* Canadian Lumber Standard   ** Oriented Strand Board

The Structural Insulated Panel (SIP) House

Architectural history can occasionally throw up some interesting surprises, not the least being the fact that Frank Lloyd Wright, one of the father figures of modern architecture in the United States, used structural insulated panels (SIPs) in some of the affordable 'Usonian' houses he designed in the late 1930s and 1940s. The concept of SIPs actually began in 1935 at the Forest Products Laboratory in Madison, Wisconsin, where engineers first speculated that plywood and hardboard sheathing could carry a portion of the structural load in wall applications. It took until 1952, however, before the first foam core SIP was created by one of Wright's students, Alden B. Dow, the son of the founder of the Dow Chemical Company. By the 1960s, rigid foam insulation products had become readily available and resulted in the production of structural insulated panels as they are known today [1].

So, what exactly is a structural insulated panel? Without becoming too technical, it is a load-bearing, sandwich construction comprised of two outer layers of timber reconstituted from sustainably sourced softwood. These facings are usually 15mm Oriented Strand Boards type 3—OSB/3, between which a layer of rigid foam insulation is fixed. The panels are manufactured offsite to precise standards to ensure they will perform as intended, with two fabrication options available: the first utilises a pre-cut rigid foam core to which adhesive is applied to the outer faces before being cold-pressed between the two facing boards; whilst the second method, known as 'autohesive bonding', requires liquid foam to be poured or injected into pre-spaced facings and which, on curing, bonds the resulting insulation material to the inner surfaces of the OSB. This insulation core stabilises the OSB and prevents deflection under loading, thereby providing the panel with the structural strength, stiffness and thermal resistance values required. Two types of foam are used to create the core: either expanded polystyrene (EPS) or polyurethane (PU), both of which are oil-based insulating foams.

Structural insulated panels can be produced in a variety of sizes and shapes (up to 1.22 metres wide and up to 7.45 metres long) and this manufacturing flexibility facilitates considerable design latitude. There are, however, many other benefits to using structural insulated panels in low-rise structures (up to four-storeys): their light weight enables their use on sites that have poor ground conditions and are thus unsuitable for masonry construction; and, being manufactured offsite, their prefabricated form means they can only be assembled one way, a valuable factor in mitigating against onsite errors. They are also fast to erect, making it possible to achieve a wind and watertight structure more quickly, thus allowing follow-on trades earlier access to the building and, overall, effecting shorter construction timescales, with commensurate reductions in site overheads. Aside from speed, there are other site pluses, not the least being fewer deliveries of materials (reducing congestion and traffic pollution), less waste (limiting the volume of material sent to landfill), and less noise.

But it is the structural and thermal properties of SIPs that provide their principal advantages over traditional forms of construction: the homogeneous building shells created with SIPs obviate the need for roof trusses or other roof structure and, being up to seven times stronger than conventional timber frames, they are excellent in dealing with in-plane loads as they act like shell structures by dispensing point loads over their entire surface area. Similarly, being free from compression problems, shrinkage or cold bridging (the panels are connected using insulated jointing splices), SIPs offer high levels of airtightness and thermal efficiency, delivering U-values as low as 0.16W per sq/m K without the need for additional insulation. Two other interesting benefits arise from the use of SIPs: the first is the reduction in the thickness of wall build-ups that can be achieved and the consequent increase in available floorspace within a fixed footprint when compared to other forms of construction; the second is the extent to which full height glazing is achievable via the thermal offset created when using panels as thick as 172mm for the external walls.

Although widely used in standard sizes by volume builders in conventional housing developments, the inherent design flexibility of structural insulated panels, together with the many benefits described above, has led to increased interest from architects in the use of this method of construction for more bespoke projects. **The House in the Woods** (2015) by architects Alma-nac is a good example: situated in an area of outstanding natural beauty (AONB) within the South Downs National Park, the brief required a contemporary home that could be adapted from single occupancy (one- bedroom) to large family gatherings (five-bedrooms). Inspiration for the 240 sq/m building was drawn from the single-storey, dual-pitch roof bungalow that had previously occupied the plot. On approach, the similar profile of the new home belies the sensitive positioning that has taken place to create a relationship with the existing mature trees on the site that provide natural control of privacy and of incoming light levels. The south, east and north elevations are faced in hand-cut bricks, with the south facing roof gables and the west elevation onto the landscaped garden are all clad with thermally modified timber.

It is the house's interiors that indicate it is not traditionally constructed. Its communal or social spaces are located on the southern end of the building, with the living room spanning the full width and punctuated on its west side with a continuous expanse of full height glazing. A large fireplace separates this focal space from the kitchen and dining areas, both of which benefit from double height ceilings that follow the dual pitch of the roof and provide a clear volume, uninterrupted by unnecessary structure. These spaces receive daylight via a large triangular area of glazing that fills the south elevation's roof gable. This spatial freedom has been made possible by the use of SIPs technology, eschewing as it does the tie-bars or other devices usually employed to hold sloping roof planes in place.

This is a large house, yet the entire superstructure of storey-height walls and roof panels was delivered to site on two lorries and erected over a period of ten days. Once in place, doors and windows were installed into factory-prepared openings in the panels. The environmental strategy for the house sought also to minimise the heating requirement in three ways: by complementing the highly insulated and airtight construction with a concrete ground floor acting as a heat sink to aid cooling in summer and warming in winter; an energy-efficient, air-

House in the Woods,
South Downs National Park
(2015)
alma-nac
Photographer: Jack Hobhouse

source heat pump to service underfloor heating within the concrete slab and supplemented by localised radiators on the first floor to boost temperatures at times of particular chill; and a wood burning stove within the living room to be fed from the almost inexhaustible supply of dead wood sourced from the grounds. The final element in this environmental package is a mechanical ventilation and heat recovery system (MVHR) to prevent the air indoors becoming stale or moisture-laden when all the windows are closed. In combination, this largely passive approach renders the decision to use SIPs in the construction of the House in the Woods both intelligent and obvious.

Not only are structural insulated panels structurally and thermally efficient, they can also be extremely economic in time and cost, as evidenced by the design and delivery of the entire project programme for a functional farmhouse at **Howe Farm** (2015) at Dorton in Buckinghamshire, by IPT Architects, being concluded within less than 12 months. This client-driven timescale included securing all necessary statutory consents, a less than straightforward hurdle to jump given that this was a greenfield site with two strict planning stipulations attached: first, that any new structure could only be used as an agricultural dwelling; and second, that convincing evidence had to be produced that the house was an intrinsic part of efforts to create a sustainable business.

The clients therefore had to meet five challenges: first, demonstrate that they could make a living from the land; second, that their house would be in keeping with the environment; third; that it would be no more than one-storey in height; fourth, that it would have no more than three bedrooms; and last, that its footprint would be contained within a plot no larger than 20m x 10m. All this before the clients' own specifications for their house could kick in.

**Howe Farm,
Buckinghamshire** (2016)
IPT Architects
Photographer: Andy Spain

Despite their tight timescale and all-in budget of £250,000, they had ambitions for an open plan living environment with views out to the farm as well as a roof deck viewing platform that could also be used for outdoor parties in Summer. Not, perhaps, the standard interpretation of what constitutes an agricultural dwelling, but one that has not only managed to meet all of the planning conditions but also fulfil the owners' ambitions for it.

It helped that IPT Architects came to the project as strong advocates of Modern Methods of Construction (MMC) and keen to challenge traditional procurement methods they see as over-complicated and expensive. The practice has a sister company—Ecospace Studios—that specialises in the design and manufacture of SIP-based buildings and the standard-sized, 1.2 x 4 metre panels used in the construction of the farmhouse were fabricated in its carpentry workshop and assembled on site in only 12 weeks. The precision-manufacturing process meant that the component parts fitted accurately, resulting in a high level of airtightness. As ever with SIPs, the structure itself is largely unseen and, at Howe Farm, is screened on all four elevations by black-stained larch cladding. Every alternate cladding board is extended upwards to form the variable-height balustrade to the roof terrace: handrail-high on the private side of the building, it drops at a shallow angle on the two perpendicular sides to roof level, and continues at this lower point along the fourth side that overlooks the fields. Contained to the single storey required, the house, with its hit-and-miss roof terrace balustrade, sits discreetly within the flat landscape.

Dark-stained cladding can also suffer from higher temperatures generated on its surface by solar gain than are measured on untreated timber or cladding that has been coated with a lighter coloured pigment. This less well-known characteristic can cause the boards to cup and/ or warp, but is avoidable if sufficient gaps are allowed for expansion and contraction, together with an adequate void behind the cladding for ventilation. The orchestration and detailing of

Howe Farm,
Buckinghamshire (2016)
IPT Architects
Photographer: Andy Spain

the cladding to the farmhouse achieves all of these things, with its dark surface given greater definition by the contrast between it and the lighter coloured western red cedar that is used for the external recessed timber surfaces, the door and window frames and throughout the interiors. Completed within budget and timescale, this is a house that, with its modular SIP construction and distinctive cladding, stands as a highly desirable, all-timber prototype that has considerable potential for adaptation to similarly sensitive sites.

As mentioned at the outset of this section, SIPs can hardly be said to constitute a new technology, having been in use in the UK in relatively conventional housing projects since the 1960s. Appreciation of their adaptability to unusual building forms is a more recent development, as is the ease with which their manufacture can be adapted to meet increasingly demanding thermal and airtightness standards. The simplicity and speed of the onsite assembly process has added to their attractiveness, with self-builders amongst their most enthusiastic users. The same might be said for those keen to build energy-efficient homes and communities at affordable prices, such as architects Gillard Associates Ltd. who, with Mulcare-Ball Developments Ltd, established LIvEco as a joint initiative to create eight dwellings at **Great House Farm** (2015) in the small community of St Fagans on the west side of Cardiff. The project is being developed in phases around the old village pond and within the historic field system, with the first phase designed to reflect the characteristics of the agricultural shed that previously occupied the site. Lifetime Homes and co-housing principles have been adopted here to help establish a sense of community, with open balconies and staircases integrated into the building's structure to provide external amenity as well as private access to the mix of one- and two-bedroom flats, three-bedroom duplexes and a two-bedroom, single storey 'pavilion'.

The decision to use SIPs for the external wall panels was heavily influenced by the ambition to achieve a very low airtightness value (1.5 air changes @ 50Pa). The SIP block is effectively sheltered beneath a lightweight, engineered truss roof supported by full-height glulam columns. Thermowood® (See Chapter 4—the Modified Timber House) has been used to form the rainscreens to the external walls and has been open-fixed horizontally on the long, garden elevation; vertically on the long facade that fronts onto the courtyard; in horizontal louvred form to conceal the grilles of the MVHR units; and as open-slatted, vertical screens positioned near stairs and entrance doors.

Great House Farm is thus very much a hybrid of timber technologies in which a traditional load-bearing timber frame, SIPs and Thermowood® form the external walls, with timber frame open-panels providing the structure of the party walls in accordance with Robust Details. The intention in combining these different timber products and systems here has not been in the pursuit of innovation: the primary objective in this first phase of building at Great House Farm has been to deliver a rugged, low-maintenance and energy-efficient building envelope in keeping with its urban fringe, semi-rural location. This, and the fact that the low energy usage achieved here more than meets Passivhaus standards, demonstrates without fuss that modest increases in specification criteria over current Building Regulation requirements, together with attention to detail in the use of standard components, can deliver sustainable homes at the affordable end of the cost spectrum.

At the opposite end of the country, the **Strathblane House** (2013), by architects ATA Studio, demonstrates the economic and other benefits that can be derived from repeated experience in the use of a specific building system. The village of Strathblane itself sits in the southwestern part of Stirlingshire, 10 miles north of Glasgow and within easy commuting distance of Scotland's largest city. It would be fair to say that rainfall in this part of Scotland can be significant even in the summer months and, with temperatures generally several degrees lower than the rather more benign climate conditions found in the south of England, the insulation aspect of SIPs construction was perhaps one of the more pressing considerations in selecting this technology for use here.

**Great House Farm,
Phase One, Cardiff** (2015)
Gillard Associates
Architecture & Design
Photographer: Alan Gillard

The Strathblane House occupies the site of a former mill that had been the oldest and most significant building in the general area. The design of the detached dwelling has therefore adopted the linear form of its predecessor and taken further advantage of the incline to the surrounding, extensive garden by having its floor plan split into three levels, thus allowing the building to nestle gently into this peaceful location. Its Glasgow-based architects have made something of a virtue of designing modern houses based on SIPs construction and this one extends the practice's application of the system by supporting the walls on a steel framed raft, the dramatic cantilever of which projects the living space out over the sloping lawn to facilitate views of the waterfall that forms part of the landscape. The house's walls and asymmetrical roof planes are formed from Kingspan's TEKHaus™ SIPs. The roof itself tilts upwards in the direction of the living room end of the house, with its deep glulam ridge beam running parallel with the eaves. Fixed at a slight angle to the vertical on the house's long elevations and perpendicular to the eaves of the inclined roof, the western red cedar cladding boards have been finished with a blue-grey transparent stain. This dynamic relationship between the house's simple rectangular form is counterbalanced by the jagged roof planes of the adjacent, detached and similarly-clad garage.

As with the other prefabricated timber frame and panel systems, further outstanding examples of the use of SIPs in contemporary house design in the UK are to be found the chapters that comprise Part Two of this book.

(1) From *'Offsite and Modern Methods of Construction—a sustainable approach'* by Dr. Robert Hairstans

Strathblane House, Strathblane, Stirlingshire (2013)
ATA Studio
Photographer: David Barbour

Chapter 3
The Solid Timber House

Houses made from solid wood have been with us since time immemorial—the log cabin is one of the earliest and simplest forms of construction known to man. The modern solid or mass timber house is, however, quite a different beast, its conception based upon a new world of laminated timber products, now commonly grouped together under the generic name of 'engineered timber'.

Today, the most commonly recognised solid timber panel product is cross laminated timber, conceived originally in the 1980s by Julius Natterer, a German engineer and professor of timber at the Ecole Polytechnique Fédérale de Lausanne. This was in response to overproduction in Switzerland's forests and a consequent surplus of low-grade timber. Natterer's innovation was to laminate wood planks together using nails, screws or dowels to form solid, one-way spanning panels: effectively glue lamination without the use of glues. This moved quickly to the idea of two-way spanning timber plates in which each wood layer was glued at right angles to the next, the final panel comprising an odd number of layers to ensure that the grain of the two outer lamellae always ran in parallel with their longest dimension. In its earliest commercial form, cross laminated timber was manufactured using a vacuum press but it did not take long before hydraulic presses were employed to produce panels in ever larger dimensions. At the beginning of this gestation process, the link between forest, sawmill and manufacturing facility was effectively umbilical, with little or no transportation and fuel requirements between each stage of the process, thereby excising most of the embodied energy costs normally associated with industrial production.

In its earliest forms, strips of wood (usually from species commonly grown in Central Europe such as spruce and fir, kiln-dried to a moisture content of 12-14% or less) were finger-jointed to form long lengths of material that could be placed side-by-side to create a large single panel layer (lamella). This was then coated with a layer of polyurethane adhesive (this solvent-free and formaldehyde-free glue sits within the '0' emission class and is able to achieve a very high quality level of adhesion with minimum risk of toxic emissions at any stage in the product's life cycle) and a second layer of wood strips laid on top at 90 degrees to the first to form the next lamella. This process continued until three, five, seven or nine layers were in place, the whole then to be fixed together with the application of hydraulic power to specific pressures calculated to ensure each panel was of defined—and consistent—structural strength, stiffness and dimensional stability. Crosswise gluing at high pressure in this way reduces the wood's expansion and shrinkage to insignificant levels.

Later, some manufacturers developed production processes whereby each wood strip was not only finger-jointed but edge-glued to the next so that each individual layer was in itself a homogeneous glued plate, capable of being lifted by suction and mechanically manoeuvred into position within the factory space—a method that dramatically reduced the physical handling

Tigh Beag,
Nethybridge,
Cairngorms National Park (2015)
SHS Burridge Architects
Photographer: Nigel Ridden

of materials and increased the size and speed at which cross laminated timber panels could be fabricated.

So much for the basic production technology. Why though has cross laminated timber captured international attention from architects, engineers, developers and building contractors? Astonishingly, there are perhaps 20 or more positive reasons that have, as a result of the emergence of solid timber construction technologies, produced a culture change in how we nowadays think about building with wood. At the outset, foremost amongst these was the ability of solid timber to sequester large amounts of atmospheric carbon dioxide throughout its constructed life: a significant environmental benefit, but one that alone was unlikely to gladden the hearts of those commercial developers and builders for whom cost factors invariably stand highest amongst their priorities. Ease and speed of construction, the possibility of reduced foundations to support lighter-weight wall, floor and roof build-ups, the need for less on-site noise and plant requirements and the generation of only small amounts of on-site waste, as well as significantly lower numbers of skilled site operatives being required to install the prefabricated panels, have all contributed to the rapid market growth of solid timber construction.

Allied with these factors are the physical properties and performance characteristics of the products: enhanced structural capacity and predictable behaviour in fire; inherent dimensional stability and material durability; acoustic and thermal contribution; offsite, precision manufacture that helps deliver high standards of airtightness; and the hygroscopic nature of wood which offers enhanced internal air quality.

Additional construction benefits include: digital design and fabrication; BIM compatibility; potential for reduced wall build-ups; speed of erection facilitating minimal on-site storage and lower on-site construction costs as well as fewer site safety issues; well-suited to modular design and manufacture; stable performance in seismic conditions; and the ability to build tall timber structures (see Chapter 12 - The Tall Timber House). Overall, the level of financial and other risk from this relatively simple building method is increasingly deemed to be lower than for other forms of construction. Solid timber is also increasingly seen to have valuable benefits for domestic house construction—its higher material costs (as against timber frame) were previously considered an impediment to its use for this building type. Again, improved understanding of circular economy arguments and the life cycle equation that permits all of the above listed factors to be assessed in combination ensures a more accurate cost comparison can be made. Given the slow speed and weather-dependent processes involved in traditional house building, solid timber construction is proving to be an increasingly attractive proposition.

One of the earliest detached solid timber houses to be built in inner London was the **Sunken House** (2007), made all the more notable in being designed by the (then) rising star (and now Sir), David Adjaye, of Adjaye Associates. The streetscape here is comprised of three-storey, semi-detached Victorian villas, the lowest floors of which are semi-sunk into the ground. In introducing a new and quite radically different house into this environment, the architect has taken design inspiration from this particular feature of these well-proportioned, brick-built dwellings and excavated the entire plot (a former builder's yard), thus creating a basement level, sunken courtyard and garden for this new, freestanding pavilion. The plan arrangement is unusual, with the lowest floor housing a photography studio, kitchen and dining space, each with access to the courtyard area. The ground floor accommodates two bedrooms and bathroom, with the house's entrance accessed via the off-street parking area that forms the roof to the studio below. A large open-plan space fills the top floor, reached via the walnut staircase that rises through the house's top-lit, triple-height hall.

Sunken House,
London Borough of Hackney
(2007)
Adjaye Associates
Photographer: Ed Reeve

The benefits of using cross laminated timber to provide the floors, load-bearing walls and roof structure of the house are made evident with this vertical disposition of spaces: the two-way spanning panels—erected in just two days—allow free placement and sizing of window

openings, a feature especially evident in the bright, white, top floor living space where a long, horizontal-format, frameless window is set flush with the external wall cladding, providing a direct view into the canopies of neighbouring mature trees and which allows evening sunlight to penetrate deep into the room. The thermal performance of the solid wood is enhanced with hemp insulation, whilst the house's exterior is clad with ribbed, western red cedar decking boards which have been stained black, a feature that allows the house to sit demurely into its site, its overall height and proportions in harmony with those of its neighbours.

Carmarthen Place, Bermondsey, London (2007)
Architects in Residence (AiR)
Photographer: Riko Hise

Built around the same time as the Sunken House, another small residential development to make early use of cross laminated timber house was constructed just south of the Thames in Bermondsey's **Carmarthen Place** (2007). In this instance, the site could have been said to be wholly unprepossessing: located behind a row of listed buildings, it was small, tightly enclosed and reached via a narrow lane. It was also L-shaped, with a curved perimeter. The design—by Architects in Residence (AiR)—took its material lead from historic, timber-clad and shuttered buildings in the area, but the structural system employed was entirely novel for the time: a solid wood cassette arrangement in which the structural panels arrived (from Slovenia) as complete units with insulation, breather membranes, battens, cladding, doors and windows pre-installed. Craned into position on the complex, multi-faceted site, the complete assembly of the project's pair of two-bedroom houses and studio took a mere 12 days. The laminated solid timber panels, manufactured from spruce grown in managed forests in Slovenia, are 100mm thick and, in the architects' words, "form the breathable structural skeleton of the building as well as the finished interior surface".

The two residential buildings are separated by a one-metre wide, triple-height void which forms the shared entrance in Carmarthen Lane. The decision to use a prefabricated timber system was both unusual and practical, the latter due to access challenges for both crane and construction and the need for speed of assembly; the former to the rare use of timber at the time as a primary structural element in a city in which the Buildings Acts had largely mitigated against it being employed for this purpose ever since the Great Fire of London in 1666. The decision to go with solid timber panels as opposed to a timber frame structure was unquestionably influenced by the availability of a modern high performance, environmentally sound system that could be manufactured off-site to very exacting specifications—not the least of which was the very unusual shape of the available plot. Externally, the two houses can be distinguished by the way they are clad: one with its Siberian larch boards fixed horizontally, whilst the same species is applied vertically to the other as single length boards, the ends articulated at each floor level with a dark shadow gap.

Still in South London, the later 75 sq/m, two-bedroom, **Strange House** (2010) in Deptford, by Hugh Strange Architects, makes clear how solid timber construction can provide an efficient solution to the redevelopment of even the most restricted of urban sites. The house is entirely hidden from view behind the tall brick perimeter wall of what had in past times supported the roof of a single-storey industrial building. The roof long gone, the site had served as a yard to a street-corner pub, until it too ceased to trade. Disused since the 1990s, the plot was bought by the architect with the intention of building a house for himself and his family within its curtilage, access being possible via an adjacent ground floor shop he had previously acquired and converted, first to a flat for himself and, later (2013), with the addition of a new extension, into a studio for his practice.

At a cost on completion (2010) of £160,000, this is an extremely low-budget house, especially for London, achieved by some very intelligent design decisions complemented by fixed-price contracts with the main subcontractors and suppliers. The first 'big ticket' design decision was to install a concrete raft on top of the existing ground slab and thereby avoid the need for costly excavations. This was made practicable by the parallel decision to form the walls and roof from cross laminated timber, ensuring the superstructure would be lighter than conventional masonry construction and not, therefore, require deep foundations.

Strange House, Deptford, South London (2010)

Hugh Strange Architects
Photographer: David Grandorge

Whilst totally enclosed, it was possible to crane the pre-cut cross laminated timber panels into the site from the residential cul-de-sac behind the boundary wall which now contains the main entrance to the house. As with other projects in this chapter, the offsite (in Switzerland) precision manufacturing technology ensured accurate, speedy and relatively quiet assembly of the panels, with little waste created during the build process. Again, the good airtightness and thermal mass inherent in this method of construction, together with high standards of insulation, minimal glazing to the north, ample natural daylight and the use of low-energy lighting and appliances, all help to reduce the building's energy requirements.

The panels themselves have their edges exposed to show their laminated composition, with no further finishing being required other than the application of a white stain and a clear wax to maintain the grain and colour of the timber. In contrast to this, the window frames, doors, internal fit-out and fixed furniture are of responsibly sourced tropical hardwood (predominantly cedro macho) that was downed by Hurricane Felix and subsequently fabricated in a Nicaraguan workshop before being shipped over in a container for site assembly. Glass is sandwiched between the exposed structural panels and the hardwood frames to form the fixed windows, the transoms to top and bottom of which, when viewed from an angle, are rendered invisible by the projecting mullions. Internally, the hardwood doors and frames are face-fixed to the structural softwood openings, thus reducing site work, accommodating tolerances and visually expressing the relationship between primary structural timber and the secondary, fit-out timber.

The fourth urban example to be included here is by one of the country's recognised masters of engineered solid timber design, Alex de Rijke of architects dRMM. The practice has long been a pioneer in the use of cross laminated timber and has, since the early years of this century, maintained a continuing programme of research investigations into the use of the material in a wide range of building types including galleries, healthcare, large-scale housing, schools and other public projects. The **WoodBlock House** (2013), whilst relatively small, sits within this experimental continuum, being a genuine design collaboration between the artist client and the architect and is in fact the practice's first completed single-family house in cross-laminated timber. It is also what nowadays is referred to as a 'live-work' building, containing as it does a large workshop and printing studio on the ground floor, spacious enough to accommodate the artist's assistants and equipment.

A narrow gap in the street-facing north elevation separates the building from its neighbour's flank wall, the passageway thus created allowing access to separate entrances to the workshop and the residential element above. Externally, this is articulated by vertically-fixed, untreated larch cladding to the ground and first floor living area, with the second floor bedroom level strikingly expressed with horizontally applied strips of plywood, painted in vivid green tones using wood block, a technique for which the artist is well known. The rear elevation to the second floor is similarly treated and, additionally, cantilevers out across the entrance passageway whilst remaining disconnected from the adjacent building. The bedrooms on this level overlook an external terrace accessed from the first floor living area. Above the second floor, and practically unseen from the street, is a small rooftop pavilion containing a studio/library.

The building's cross laminated structure has been left exposed throughout and, in the residential levels, reflects the natural light that reaches deep into the open living area and rear bedrooms. The bonuses gained from using this technology in such a constricted urban location, however, have been the speed with which the panels were erected, plus the elimination of wet trades and the significant reductions made possible in construction noise, pollution, site traffic and waste compared to other forms of construction. These, coupled with the acknowledged sustainability and carbon storage benefits inherent in cross laminated timber, eloquently make the case for far greater use of engineered timber products in the design of mixed-use inner city developments.

The benefits of solid timber construction for new housing are not only being realised in dense urban situations—an increasing number of projects are emerging in suburban areas that demonstrate the constructional and spatial versatility possible with this technology. Part of the Greater London conurbation, Woodford is a relatively wealthy suburb situated approximately 9.5 miles (15.3km) north-east of London's Charing Cross and a short distance from the south-western boundary of Epping Forest. Sited within this area is **Mazarin House** (2014), a four-storey development of six two-bedroom apartments enclosed to its south and west by large, detached 1930s homes and to the north and east by blocks of flats dating from the 1970s. Shoehorning the project into the available plot shape has resulted in a multi-faceted building and an even more complex arrangement of roof planes—the latter in fact providing inspiration for its name. Grandly titled 'Mazarin House', the moniker refers to the 17th century method of cutting diamonds to produce 17 faces on the upper crown and which is considered to be the first true 'brilliant' cut. With its 17 cross laminated timber roof planes arranged in non-orthogonal fashion to optimise the internal spaces below, the connection between Mazarin House's sculpted form and the gem cutters' art is perhaps not so fanciful as it might initially seem. More, possibly, than any of the previous houses in this chapter, this development, by Arboreal Architects, has sought to maximise the potential inherent in the computer numeric control (CNC) of the machine tools used in the CLT factory to translate the designers' 3D computer models of the building into a precise kit of solid timber parts.

As an example of digital design and fabrication being used to directly manufacture the continuous, airtight shell of a sizeable building that is both spatially and formally complex, Mazarin House gives some indication of solid timber construction's wider potential—straightforward and quick to assemble; capable of supporting a continuous external layer of thermal insulation (thereby avoiding penetration by other elements that can cause cold bridging); and economically and thermally efficient. With the surfaces of its cross laminated timber roof planes exposed internally in each of the top floor apartments and the building's exterior faced on all sides with an open-jointed, Siberian larch rain screen horizontally mounted on larch battens, this is a building that takes full advantage of the engineered timber and other wood products now available and demonstrates considerable design confidence in their use. In a housebuilding sector in England in which brick and block construction still predominates, Mazarin House, with its NHBC Warranty, offers an indication that consumer, developer, funder and insurer perceptions are beginning to move towards recognition of the benefits of modern, engineered timber construction.

Mazarin House, Woodford, East London (2014)
Arboreal Architecture
Photographer: Tom Raymont

**Dune House,
Thorpeness, Suffolk** (2010)

Jarmund Vigsnaes AS Arkitekter
MNAL in association with Mole
Architects

Photographer: Jarmund Vigsnaes
AS Arkitekter / MNAL

A similarly complex arrangement of roof forms renders the **Dune House** (2010) instantly identifiable to visitors seeking the third built project of Living Architecture, a non-profit organisation set up by Alain de Botton to promote the virtues of modern architecture. To date, the writer has commissioned eight outstanding architectural practices to design a string of distinctive holiday homes. Situated just south of the picturesque Suffolk village of Thorpeness, a designated Area of Outstanding Natural Beauty, the multi-award winning design by Norwegian practice Jarmund/Vigsnaes Arkitekter (in association with Cambridge-based Mole Architects) turns convention on its head by placing the house's visible structural form above a ground floor that is fully glazed on all sides. The resulting arrangement gives the impression—especially at night—of an unsupported pitched and gabled roofscape that floats in the air. The vertical gables are clad with dark stained Scandinavian whitewood boards to reflect the vernacular of traditional local houses.

So why this unusual arrangement? Its form, according to its authors, "derives from a wish to echo local traditions while providing something 'refreshingly new' and from memories of childhood holidays in England spent in the attic bedrooms of gable-roofed B&Bs". This, however, hardly accounts for the extraordinary plan arrangement of the upper floor in which four bedrooms with en-suite bathrooms are skewed into the house's overall rectangular footprint in a fiercely complex arrangement of angled and intersecting dividing walls. The ground floor plan, slightly sunken to provide a sense of privacy and a degree of protection from the bracing North Sea wind, has a more conventional open plan layout and gives no indication whatsoever of the seemingly anarchic room shapes above. Further investigation makes clear the house's strong connection to its site: the fully-glazed ground floor provides a 360° panoramic view of the flat surrounding landscape and across the sea to the distant horizon. Upstairs, each bedroom—and the bathtub within it—is directionally positioned to respond to a pre-ordained view. Internally, the cross laminated timber has been left exposed, its surfaces given a light wash of white wood wax oil and a transparent fire-resistant coating.

All of this spatial magic has been made possible by the architects' previous experience in the use of cross laminated timber and a sound appreciation of its potential to form unusual spaces without any interruptive supporting structure. The precision-cutting technology used to prefabricate solid timber panels means that the awkward geometries that would normally require complicated, difficult to form junctions are here edge-profiled to ensure the necessary accuracy and overall airtightness. As with the Mazarin House, it has been possible to insulate the unusually shaped panels on their outer surfaces to avoid difficult to solve thermal bridging problems. In the case of the Dune House, however, this is taken to new heights—literally—by raising the solid wood structure in its entirety into the air on an in-situ reinforced concrete service core / first floor slab and slender steel perimeter columns.

A very different approach to the emerging 'elevated-cross-laminated-timber-box-with-multiple-tilted-triangular-roof planes' genre is the **Sussex House** (2015), by Wilkinson King Architects. With sweeping views through floor-to-ceiling glazing across the flat, meadowed landscape towards the South Downs, the building, as with the Dune House, concentrates all of its public spaces on the ground floor—in this instance with three of its four bedrooms above and only the guest suite situated on the ground floor. The upper box projects forward over the glazing, supported on its leading edge by a row of slim, cruciform steel columns, providing a degree of shade from southern sunlight. The house is actually entered from a courtyard and formal garden on its north side through a large glazed area set within the solid facade, the view from here completely clear through to the landscape beyond.

Once inside, a top-lit, double-height reception area raises the eye to the inclined cross laminated timber ceiling planes and wall construction of the house's upper level. A beautifully-detailed cantilevered staircase, formed from the same material and set within a glazed, north-facing box, leads to the simple corridor access to bedrooms. The corridor itself gives the first indication of the rhythm of the exposed CLT ceiling, but it is only within the rooms that the three-dimensional contribution the folded roof makes to each of these spaces becomes clear: the walls of the en-suite bathrooms stop short of the ceiling, with glazed infill panels allowing the roof to be read as a continuous form, whilst also providing necessary environmental separation. The solid timber panels have been lacquered throughout with Envirograf, a fire retardant that prevents surface spread of flame and which has also softened the colour of the wood from its natural state.

**Downley House,
South Downs National Park**
(2012)
Birds Portchmouth Russia
Photographer: Christopher Taee

Externally, the upper floor and adjacent garage are clad horizontally with elegantly proportioned panels of western red cedar boarding that have already mellowed to silver-grey. Inset into the south facing bedroom elevation are small, sliding pocket windows concealed by louvred shutters. The latter provides shade from strong light whilst the former can be opened to their full width in summer, giving the rooms an almost Mediterranean quality. A world apart from conventional housebuilding techniques, the precision detailing and construction of the cross laminated timber box and roof, together with the crisp, modular appearance of the cladding, instead confers the quality of finely detailed carpentry on the construction of the Sussex House.

Another home that moves solid wood construction into new and innovative areas lies within the South Downs National Park Area of Outstanding Natural Beauty itself. **Downley House** (2012) is part of the Ditchley Park estate. Prior to its construction, the site had been the location of the estate engineer's house, but its appearance had long ago been reduced to that of a ruined entrance elevation. The architects, Birds Portchmouth Russum, were selected as a result of an informal design competition run by the client, an instrumental element in their success being the decision to integrate the wall into the overall development of house and landscape.

The finished building is a tour de force of architectural composition, with the family and guest wings of this five-bedroom home arranged on either side of the building's most unusual feature: a dining hall in the tradition of medieval country homes that, unusually, takes its elliptical form from that of the giant oak barrels known as foudres, each capable of holding 600 litres (132 gallons) of wine. The clients had previously worked in the wine industry and the discovery of this fact led the architects to this inspirational solution. This, and the two top-glazed staircase silos that sit symmetrically on either side of the hall, are not only the most distinctive elements of the house, they are also the ones that demonstrate another development in solid wood construction. Ordinarily, most solid wood elements—whether formed from glued, dowelled or nailed laminations—are large flat plates of timber. Here, the cross laminated timber takes a different shape altogether, the dining hall being a structured shell of curved cross laminated timber panels on curved glulam (glued laminated timber) ribs, the latter set at tilting angles to deliver even greater impact. The tightly curved cross laminated timber panels that enclose the spiral staircases were surely an even more exacting technical departure for the Swiss manufacturer but, together with the other solid wood elements, assembly into the basic shell of the house took a mere six weeks after their arrival on site.

Very much a hybrid in which natural materials indigenous to the location have been combined with modern products to picturesque effect, the foudre hall is very much the heart of the house, clearly expressing the solid timber credentials that elsewhere internally are concealed behind plaster and externally by local stone, oak boards or render.

Before leaving this chapter, mention should also be made of two other forms of solid timber construction highlighted at the outset:, the latter known in Europe (where it originated) as Brettstapel. Interest in both forms has been shown by architects and others with concerns about adhesives or other potentially toxic content in construction materials and products materials.

Nail laminated timber—or Nail-Lam—is possibly the simplest and most easily manufactured form of non-glued lamination and while well established, especially for larger span structures in countries such as Canada, this form of construction is barely known in the UK, with only a few examples built to date—and even those being only small elements of the whole building. Historically, this simple method of construction was used by carpenters and timber manufacturing companies—whether on- or off-site—to assemble curved roofs and other bespoke structures. Nowadays sophisticated nailing equipment is available which, with the use of aluminium nails, allows CNC-machining to be carried out without damage to the cutting

**Plummerswood,
Innerleithen,
Scottish Borders** (2011)

Gaia Architects
Photographer: Michael Wolchover

blades. It can, however, be a very low-tech method of manufacturing solid timber panels, a process well suited to localised production—a bonus in rural areas and, with no commercial manufacturing of nail laminated timber currently taking place in the UK, is an opportunity the forest and timber processing sectors continue to explore. The very nature of of their fabrication means, however, that nail laminated elements are not in themselves airtight, nor do they provide significant sound reduction values and thus these panels require additional layers in wall, floor and roof build-ups.

Dowel laminated timber also dispenses with the need for adhesives by using hardwood dowels to bind the laminations together. In this method, stacked planks are bound together by inserting the dowels into pre-drilled holes in the lamellae. The system makes use of the differences in moisture content (MC) in the two types of wood employed: the dowel being made from a hardwood species (such as beech) with an MC of around 8%, whilst the planks have been kiln dried down to an MC between 12-15%. The hardwood dowels, seeking moisture equilibrium, swell and expand within the drilled holes and, in doing so, lock the panel elements together. Far from being some recent technological discovery, this can be regarded as a panellised application of a traditional timber frame construction technique in which wooden pegs were inserted into joints into green timber posts and beams, in the knowledge that the drying process would ensure tight connections were formed. In modern, factory-based production of dowel laminated timber, the hardwood dowels are inserted either perpendicular to the orientation of the stacked planks or diagonally, the latter obtaining a stronger bond due to its ability to reduce movement in the lamellae. As the process does not involve hydraulic presses to ensure tight bonds are achieved, dowel laminated timber panels are usually significantly thicker than cross laminated timber one.

It should be emphasised that the descriptions of nail laminated timber and dowel-laminated timber manufacture offered here are necessarily brief and are not intended as comparisons—whether good or bad—with cross laminated timber. In terms of solid timber construction, the latter, a two-way spanning structural technology, has found more applications than its non-glued colleagues. As yet, there are only a handful of dowel laminated timber buildings in the UK, a notable example being **Plummerswood** (2011), a detached house hidden away at the end of a series of private and public access tracks in the Scottish Borders. Designed by Gaia Architects, the practice had gained previous experience of Austrian-manufactured Brettstapel panels on a remote primary school at Acharacle in the west of Scotland and chose to use the same system for this two-storey house. The building's master bedroom and sitting room are contained within a cube-shaped element, itself connected by a double height entrance hall to a curved section that contains two of its three bedrooms, a kitchen-dining room, study and workshop. With its combination of super-insulation and exemplary airtightness levels, as well as being oriented on its steeply-sloping site to optimise daylight and solar gain, the house was designed to meet Passivhaus standards. The architects, however, prefer to refer to it as an 'active house' since its healthy indoor air quality has been achieved through manual rather than automatic operation of the ventilation system. Internally, the fixed furnishings were a result of collaboration between Gaia Architects and the designer-makers at the locally-based Real Wood Studios. Externally, the house's open-jointed cladding makes use of locally-grown European larch, its separate horizontal and vertical installation used to distinguish the two main forms of the house.

The use of solid timber construction systems is now well established in the UK for a wide range of building types and, as ever-greater numbers of architects, engineers and other construction professionals and contractors gain experience of them, so too will their use expand. This is nowhere more so than in house building, a sector that has been slow to recognise the merits of these relatively new technologies. Government financial and other incentives established in response to continual demand for new houses, coupled with the need to reduce energy costs, is likely to see this situation change dramatically and, in the near future, the solid timber house may very well be seen as the model for all to aspire to.

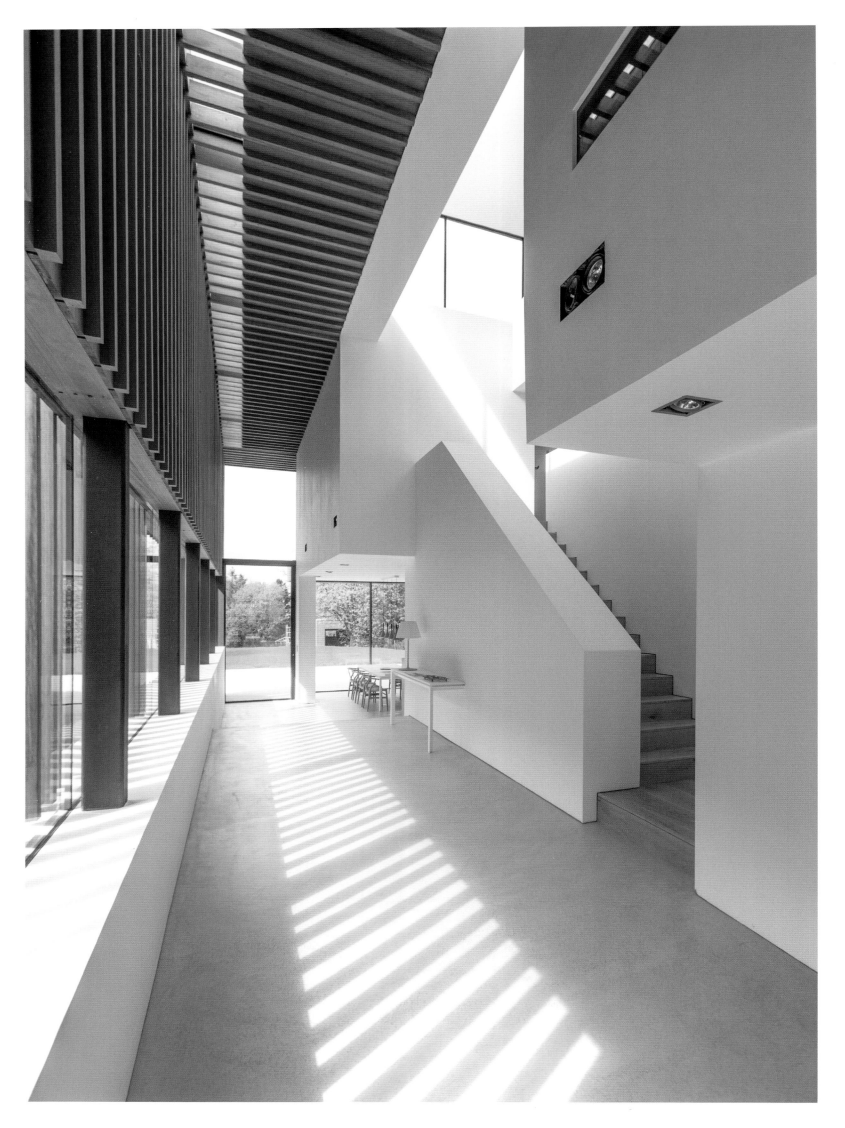

Chapter 4
The Modified Timber House

Wood modification may be a term unfamiliar to many, but the concept of altering the characteristics of low grade and/or low durability timber in order to improve its performance and service life has been around for a very long time. The technology necessary to carry out different methods of wood modification actually developed many years ago, but it is only relatively recently that some have become commercially viable. These processes predominantly involve the chemical or thermal modification of the cell structure of the selected wood species to create timber products that have very different mechanical and physical properties to those of the raw material they are manufactured from. Paradoxically, it is this application of science that has possibly contributed to a lack of understanding amongst construction professionals of what constitutes a modified timber product and how it might be used, with related market confusion caused by multiple, different processes and product types. These factors have proved to be barriers to the use of modified timbers that have a high entry price and for which the enhanced value of their characteristics is too often measured solely on capital cost rather than long-term performance. Nevertheless, the market for these products continues to grow as their benefits become increasingly apparent.

Before exploring the different modified timber products currently available and the processes by which they are manufactured, it is useful to understand the reasons why they have come to the fore in recent years. The environmental issues relating to tropical rain forest depletion are well-known and whilst the provision of timber from these sources to the global construction marketplace is but one part of this story, the climate change implications and landscape destruction involved have led to legislation and regulations in many countries that affect the importation of hardwood species from forests unable to demonstrate, through recognised certification schemes such as FSC and PEFC, that they are being sustainable managed. Many tropical hardwoods do come from properly certified sources, but there is sufficient confusion and/or lack of knowledge on this subject amongst architects and other construction industry professionals in the UK for there to be a widely held impression that the specification and use of all tropical hardwoods is illegal.

This has led to new opportunities for modified timber products precisely because they exhibit many of the main characteristics of tropical hardwoods, notably high durability against biological and fungal degradation (particularly important in Use Class 3 conditions), as well as the ability to inhibit wood's natural tendency to shrink, swell and warp in different humidity conditions. Coupled with these benefits is their manufacture from material that has not only come from certified forest sources, but which also makes use of low-grade wood and/or non-durable species. An added factor is that an increasing number of specifiers are nowadays suspicious of available preservative treatments and, rather than risk possible deterioration in untreated or uncoated timber, have sought renewable, bio-based material alternatives to concrete, plastic and steel which, due to the high levels of energy used in their manufacture and their inability to

**Edge Hill, Ponteland,
Northumberland** (2015)

Sutherland Hussey
Harris Architects

Photographer: Colin Harris /
SUHUHA

store large amounts of carbon, are significantly less attractive options. In this context, investing the substrate of faster-growth timber with qualities (including dimensional stability and increased hardness) more typical of old-growth, but non-sustainable, tropical hardwoods makes modified timber a compelling option.

So, how exactly is wood modified? Essentially, there are two approaches: thermal modification and chemical modification. Without delving into the more abstruse areas of science involved, the basic method of thermal modification involves heating the host species to a temperature in excess of 160°C, a process carried out in an environment in which oxygen is restricted or eliminated to prevent the wood charring. Various methods are used by different manufacturers to exclude oxygen: the first and most common, was first developed in Finland and is generally marketed under the Thermowood® brand name. It requires green timber—usually Scandinavian pine or spruce—to be heated to between 220-240°C to create a veil of steam that protects the wood during the process. This is a patented, gradual technique that reduces the stresses caused by high temperatures on the chemical and physical elements of the product and results in the manufacture of two grades of material Thermo-D (suitable for Durability Class 2 applications) and Thermo-S (suitable for Durability Class 3 applications), with the former having a guaranteed service life of at least 30 years when durability against decay is considered.

A second thermal modification method—referred to as hydrothermal modification—is used to produce Platowood®. This involves a five stage process which differs from other thermal modification methods in that there is no loss of flexibility in the material due to it being carried out at lower temperatures and also to the additional heating and drying stages involved, a benefit that means longer and wider boards can be produced without risk of movement in the material.

The different thermal modification methods described here have one thing in common: the avoidance of any chemicals in their production with only heat and steam involved. By contrast, chemical modification involves the use of bio-based liguids to effect permanent transformation in the cell structure of the wood. The two main products commercially available are Accoya® and Kebony®, each of which involves a different, patented manufacturing process: that of Accoya® uses acetic anhydride in a process known as acetylation, whilst Kebony® uses furfuryl acohol, a waste by-product of sugar cane production. Both are manufactured using timber sourced from sustainable forests (in the case of Accoya®, much of the initial product was developed using Radiata pine, but a wider range of species is now employed; Kebony® is manaufactures from Ash, Beech, Maple, Nordic pine, Scots pine and Southern yellow pine as the base species).

Heron Court, Thamesmead
(2010)
Bell Phillips Architects
Photographer: Kilian O'Sullivan

Key to the success of all these methods and products is their extended durability, dimensional stability, increased hardness, consistent quality through the wood, mould and insect resistance, no added biocides and thus no disposal phase problems. The questions, therefore, for specifiers and end users, are when, where and which to use?

An early example of Thermowood® use in housing can be found in Thamesmead, an area developed in the1960s to rehouse families from inner south London. Built on flood-prone marshland on the south side of the Thames, the early phases of what was intended to become—to all intents and purposes—a new town, the plan for Thamesmead was based upon the design principles for housing estates first established in 1929 at Radburn in New Jersey. To counter Thamesmead's somewhat disadvantageous location, major new river defences, balance ponds, canals and storm drains were carefully integrated into its original masterplan with the aim of enriching peoples' enjoyment of the landscape. Sadly, these laudable intentions for the area were undone by the inadequate infrastructure, poor transport service, inflexible social housing tenure arrangements and the lack of provision of essential facilities such as shops.

Almost 25 years of hit-and-miss attempts to regenerate the existing housing assets followed the Greater London Council's demise in 1986 before a range of new-build projects began to be commissioned. **Heron Court** (2010), by Bell Phillips Architects, is a mixed residential project comprising 12 rental flats and duplexes in a three-storey block on the west side of the site with a linked four-storey block sitting at an angle to its east and which contains six 'Rent to Buy' homes. The whole development faces onto a communal garden to the west and a canal to the east. Due to the long-established risk of flood, the ground floors of the buildings have been constructed with concrete frames and brick skins, whilst the wall structures above are formed from lightweight steel frames with vertically-fixed Thermowood® cladding. The material is applied as flat, uninterrupted planes to the gable ends of each block, in contrast to the long elevations, where a regular series of timber fins project from the facades to support the balconies and walkways. At second floor level, the flats are accessed via wide walkways that function as open loggias inset behind steel and timber screens. This level can effectively be read as the attic storey of a classically-ordered, tripartite elevation, but it is the extensive use of a durable, dark-brown timber product—Thermowood®—in this moisture-rich environment that defines the scheme and provides it with the quality and longevity necessary to transcend the unfortunate reputation of the area's planning.

From the south of the Thames to the north-east of England, and a giant step from the world of social housing to a highly individual detached property on the exclusive Darras Hall estate at Ponteland in Northumberland. The plot sizes and ratios on the estate are strictly controlled and, with by-laws designed to preserve open spaces and prevent industry or commercial buildings being constructed in the village, most residents live in original 1960s or 70s houses or have bought a plot with the intention of replacing the existing dwelling with a new home. The owners of **Edge Hill** (2015), by Sutherland Hussey Harris Architects, opted for the latter course and, as a result, now have an extraordinarily bold private family home that could hardly be more different from its predecessor on the site: a poor quality post-war bungalow. Situated towards the front of its long, narrow plot, the two-storey house has a conventional, rectangular footprint upon which a precast concrete structure, with large triple-glazed windows at each end of the building and a monopitch zinc roof has been constructed.

So far, so straightforward, but it is the way in which thermally modified timber has been used in the construction of this house that makes it stand out. Most examples of thermally modified timber begin life as softwoods or non-durable hardwoods, with the heat process transforming them into hard, durable materials. As well as using domestically grown softwoods and hardwoods, the European timber market also imports a wide range of hardwoods from sustainably managed forests on other continents for which new or alternative uses are continually sought. Modern timber engineering and modification processes are thus increasingly being applied to non- or moderately-durable species from this extensive resource to develop new, high added value products for use in the construction sector.

Heron Court, Thamesmead (2010)
Bell Phillips Architects
Photographer: Kilian O'Sullivan

Edge Hill, Ponteland, Northumberland (2015)
Sutherland Hussey Harris Architects
Photographer: Colin Harris / SUHUHA

Such is the case at Edge Hill, where Natural Cladding's® thermally modified product has been used: manufactured from non-durable Obeche from west Africa, the process has transformed the highest of the species' three grades—Ayous—into a highly durable material that has outstanding levels of stability.

A wrap-around concertina of frames fabricated from this thermally modified product extends the entire length of the building and finds full expression in it's interior: a glass door in a double-height transparent screen on the west side of the front elevation leads into a cloister-like, grand corridor and an uninterrupted view to, and through, an equivalent glazed portal at the other end of the house to the extensive landscaped garden beyond. The rhythmic timber frames sits on a continuous precast concrete plinth on the house's west side, with the spaces between the ribs open to light and views into the side garden. At head-height level, the ribs increase in depth and the spaces between are boarded rather than glazed to give thickness to the wall, before folding to form the roof structure over the wide, cloistered passage. Fenestration appears again between the, now horizontal, ribs to bring light deep into the house. The effect is striking: the play of light and shade in the long hallway brings an ever-changing richness to the clean, elegant lines of the building's modernist interior. The relationship between the thermally modified, straight-grained and knot-free hardwood and the white plaster walls is symbiotic and one in which masterly craftsmanship has brought this highly restrained palette of materials into beautiful expression.

Edge Hill, Ponteland, Northumberland (2015)
Sutherland Hussey Harris Architects
Photographer: Colin Harris / SUHUHA

Back to the south of England and to East Sussex's Upper Rother Valley, where **Old Bearhurst** (2011), by Duggan Morris Architects, sits within a designated Area of Outstanding Natural Beauty (AONB). The brief for the extension to the 200 year old oast house and barn that had previously been converted to dwelling use was nothing if not ambitious: the architects were required to respect the old buildings and, in doing so, to 'rediscover their integrity' when forming a new annex to them; to invest the remodelled home with character and personality; and to take advantage of the views across the valley to the south and to the villages of Burwash and Burwash Weald that are visible on the ridge. Not unusual requirements, perhaps—indeed, most of these points could likely be found in the original briefs for other rural houses featured in this book—but the difference here lay in how to marry a large modern extension to the strong agricultural forms of the oast house and barn, traditional working buildings synonymous with this part of England.

In addressing this design conundrum, the architects very clearly immersed themselves not only in the architectural history of the region and of the specific buildings at Old Bearhurst, but also in the complexities of the multifarious, overlapping local and national planning policies relating to the design of new houses within green belt land, in order to arrive at a solution satisfactory to all. This is not to suggest compromise, but instead to make clear that the architects' rigorous analysis resulted in a design that more than fulfilled the local council's requirement *"...that extensions do not dominate the existing dwelling but, rather, are visually subservient to it and hence add to, and do not detract from, its character and appearance."*

Old Bearhurst,
East Sussex (2011)
Duggan Morris Architects
Photographer: James Brittain

The project as carried out has two distinct elements: one being the original building with its oast and roundels, and the second being the lower extension, with the contrast between the pair expressed through the articulation of form and in the materials. In plan terms, the large extension is located over the footprint of removed outbuildings and is slightly sunk into into the ground in deference to the repaired and sensitively upgraded historic structures. The sculptural geometries of the addition have been give three-dimensional form by the use of structural insulated panels (SIPs), the technology chosen to deliver a thermally efficient, well-sealed envelope and clad with a rainscreen of Platowood® Frake´ boards that rise up and over the interlocking roofscapes. Frake´ is a fast-growing hardwood that originates from sustainably managed forests in West Africa and has a flawless surface with a flame-like patterned grain that is accentuated by the Platowood® process. This characteristic is further highlighted in the way the product is used at Old Bearhurst, where the sharply cut mitres between the wall and roof boards provide a strong, modern contrast to the rough-sawn, shiplapped green oak cladding that was added between the first floor level and the eaves of the barn during its remodelling. Since the extension's construction, the Platowood® has mellowed relatively evenly in colour, giving it's clustered forms a patina of age that successfully complements the materials of the original buildings. When the clients for Old Bearhurst asked their architects to *"create a dwelling that, over time, would come to reflect an exemplar approach to rural renovation work"* they surely could not have anticipated how determined their design team would be to deliver just such a paradigm.

**Old Bearhurst,
East Sussex** (2011)
Duggan Morris Architects
Photographer: James Brittain

Completed a year before Old Bearhurst, **The Haven** (2010) at Horning on the Norfolk Broads by Lambert Scott & Innes (LSI) Architects is an early, unusual use of Accoya®. The house is surrounded on three sides by water judged to be 'Flood Zone 3' (an area most likely to flood), a designation that would normally preclude any development, but discussions with the Broads Authority and the Environment Agency resulted in the architects' design solution being accepted and planning permission granted. Aside from the possibility of rising water levels (a challenge met here by raising the house on stilts, a semi-disguised structural solution that gives the impression of the two-storey building floating over the landscape), the level of moisture content in the atmosphere in this part of the world is high and generally constant, conditions that demand the use of highly durable and dimensionally stable materials. Hence the decision to maximise the use of Accoya® in the construction of the house.

**The Haven,
Horning,
Norfolk** (2010)
Lambert Scott & Innes
Photographer: Richard Osborne

Other, practical issues influenced the building's specification and construction: seeking high levels of airtightness and thermal performance, the architects elected for prefabricated timber frame closed panels which, due to the restricted road access into the site, had to be delivered by river barge. So too were the curved Accoya® glulam beams that screen the rear of the house and enclose the building's circulation ramp. The curved glulam elements wrap over the rectilinear box that contains the living accommodation and, in their support of the roof, allude to the timber ribs that form the skeleton of traditionally-built boats.

A more literal expression of this can be seen in the form of the low boathouse that stands alongside and which also serves as the Haven's energy centre. Accoya® cladding boards are fixed horizontally to all four sides of the boathouse and to the accommodation pavilion, but it is the fabrication of the curved glulam that is most remarkable here: the bulk of early external uses of modified timber were limited to cladding and decking, but the design and specification of the Haven necessitated bespoke laminated elements to be made from acetylated wood. A request to carry out a commission of this sort would be a challenge for many UK manufacturers of timber products even today, but Newnham and Abel Structures Ltd in North Walsham rose admirably to the task.

Following manufacture, the Accoya® glulam and cladding elements were both hand-finished with WoodGuard Color Professional, a protective, merbau-coloured coating that penetrates all the wood fibres without altering the material's structure and natural appearance. The primary reasons for its use on the Haven are its water-repellant properties, its very high UV resistance and its ability to slow the visible ageing of the wood. The final result is a house that in its design, fabrication and construction is very much of its place but not of its time: the architects of the Haven were surely prescient in anticipating the advanced technical developments in Accoya®-based products that are increasingly being seen in mainstream use.

The Haven, Horning, Norfolk (2010)
Lambert Scott & Innes
Photographer: Richard Osborne

Dunsmore House (2012)

Neil Sutherland Architects /
MAKAR Ltd

Photographer: MAKAR Ltd

Indeed, in seeking to extend the market opportunities for Accoya®, its manufacturers, Accsys Technologies PLC, have continuously explored innovative applications for the acetylation process that look beyond cladding and decking solutions. The Netherlands-based group has been instrumental in pushing forward new options and possibilities for its particular version of modified timber, including testing the material's long-term durability and general performance in lining canal walls and in a range of large and small bridges in the Netherlands that are in direct contact with water. A small, low-tech research and development exercise with similar aims formed part of the design and construction of **Dunsmore House** (2012), at Ardross in the Scottish Highlands, some 30 miles north of Inverness. Designed and built by Neil Sutherland Architects/MAKAR Ltd., this combined architecture and construction company produces (almost exclusively) ecological homes that are predominantly manufactured from locally-grown timbers such as Douglas fir, Scots pine, Scottish-grown larch and Sitka spruce. The company has also developed its own heavily insulated, closed panels that are designed work in conjunction with the large-section, platform timber frame structural system MAKAR prefabricates in its own workspace near the Highland capital. Such is the construction of Dunsmore House.

Set within a south-facing woodland site, the semi-detached, larch-clad building was designed as a self-build for two families, with each home's open-plan living accommodation placed at first floor level to gain maximum solar benefit and to facilitate distant views. Service areas and bedrooms are located on the ground floor. In order to have minimal impact on the land, each house is supported on eight shallow pad foundations from which concrete posts project to support ground beams. These longitudinal timber elements are well-protected from rain but, although the risk of permanent wetting leading to decay was relatively low, concern that seasonal shrinkage and swelling of the beams could affect the level of the building led to the development of glue-laminated beams made from acetylated timber. Once installed, the Accoya® beams underwent an extended period of monitoring by Edinburgh Napier University's Centre for Offsite Construction and Innovative Structures (COCIS), using strain gauges to assess whether any settling over time had taken place. The results indicated good performance with virtually no movement, the conclusion being that the acetylated ground beam solution could be used beneficially in many instances instead of the continuous strip foundations that are the norm for so much of the housing built in the UK today. Not only would this offer considerable economies in time and construction materials, but potentially also save some 2000 Kg carbon dioxide EQ per house, a massive reduction in the sector's impact on the environment.

Sixty miles southeast within the part of the Scottish Highlands embraced by the Cairngorms National Park, **Tigh Beag** (2015), by SHS Burridge Architects, sits in a small, picturesque village on the well-trafficked tourist route between Aviemore and Grantown-on Spey: this is the road north into Speyside distillery country. Building a home in one of Scotland's two national parks can be especially challenging: not only are there strong environmental protection measures in place and strict planning restrictions on the numbers and locations where houses can be built, but weather conditions, especially in the Cairngorms, can also be severe: strong to gale force winds, driving rain and snow, coupled with long, dark winter months are facts of life here, offset by the rugged beauty of the mountain landscape and, on sunnier summer days, glorious views. Houses need to be robust in this environment, as evidenced by the traditional, solid construction of the single-storey cottages and detached houses that punctuate the wooded road leading to Tigh Beag.

Not that it's possible to miss this particular home—its form and colour easily distinguish it from its neighbours and surroundings, yet every part of its design has been rationally conceived. In this well-forested area, the availability of natural light is paramount and was the principal driver of the house's orientation, internal layout, window locations and energy strategy. Set on an east-west axis with large windows to the south and minimal openings to the north to maximise solar gain and minimise heat loss, the fenestration is positioned to track the sun according to the way the building is used during the day. This is reinforced by Tigh Beag's inverted section: the bedrooms are located on the ground floor and have small, east facing windows to catch early morning light, whilst the first floor above has one substantial volume, its generous living area expanded into the roof and provided with additional natural illumination via a series of skylight windows. The floor area on this level is broken into a series of spaces inflected by the stepped facade, each with its own associated window.

the determination to maximise the ingress of light is also a key aspect of the strategy to make Tigh Beag an energy-efficient, sustainable dwelling which, although designed for extended use with provision for homeworking, needed also to be able to support intermittent occupation. The house's primary structure is formed from cross laminated timber which, in the (still) absence of a UK manufacturer using locally-grown material, was supplied from Mayr-Melnhof Holz's plant in southern Austria. The building is heavily insulated and, with triple-gazed windows, lobbied entrances and excellent airtightness, has space heating demand of only 17kWH per sq/m per year. The most striking aspect of the house, however, is its brightly-coloured outer skin of horizontally-fixed, tongue and groove Accoya® boards, each or which has undergone vacuum paint treatment at Russwood's Newtonmore premises, less than 30 miles away. This specialist, three-stage process (primer, first coat and second) gives an even, 150 micron, sealed colour-coating to each of the board surfaces, offering greater durability than conventional spray methods. The colour choice at Tigh Beag responds particularly well to the special quality of light found in this part of the Cairngorms, with its uniform finish drawing the house's faceted vertical surfaces and eaves angles crisply together against the wilder background landscape.

Another application of the acetylation process used in the manufacture Accoya® that should be mentioned is also one that many may consider to be an unlikely direction: the modification of medium density fibreboard (MDF) to produce a durable and dimensionally stable panel product. The combination of acetylated wood fibre with the technology used to manufacture normal MDF has resulted in a version of the material that has quite different properties from its forebear, not the least being the acetylation of sustainable raw materials and a high-performance resin with zero added formaldehyde in its formulation, the combination of which makes the product suitable for use in environmentally sensitive situations. Marketed as Medite®Tricoya®Extreme, the product has several other benefits that considerably widen the range of potential applications for it in construction: it is light weight and comes with a guarantee of up to 50 years in above ground use and 25 years if used in ground contact: both realistic service life timescales for outdoor conditions.

**Tigh Beag,
Nethybridge,
Cairngorms National Park** (2015)
SHS Burridge Architects
Photographer: Nigel Ridden

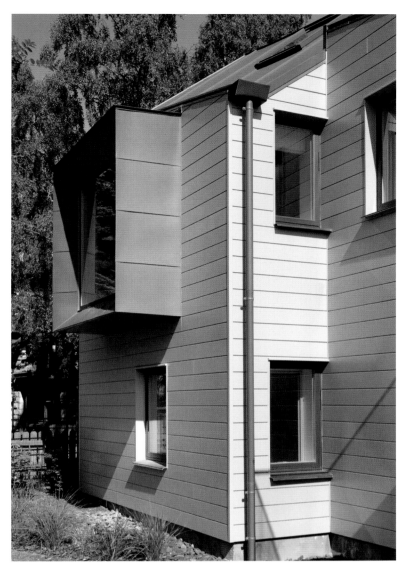

First launched in 2012, there are still relatively few UK examples of the product being used externally on housing projects, a factor that has possibly more to do with the slow recovery of the construction sector, post-2008, and a fluctuating and conservative housing market than any lack of quality or potential uses for this thermally modified panel product. One such, however, is the **Periscope House** (2014), in the Norfolk village of Honingham, by Studio Bark Architects, a practice with a particularly strong environmental ethos. Built on virgin land that looks to the south with a gentle slope towards the River Tud, the architectural response to site's characteristics is plainly evident in the two, cedar-clad periscopic balconies that not only frame views across the valley, but which are also aligned to summer and winter sun angles to provide passive solar shading. The house's low-energy strategy does not end there: the courtyard created between the two wings has minimised the plan depth of the building which, in combination with a substantial GGBS concrete trombe´ wall and stair and a high level rooflight, provides a low impact, season-specific passive heating and cooling system.

The house's sustainable timber credentials are strong: the horizontally-fixed western red cedar cladding used at first floor level was sourced from woodlands within 500 metres of the site and milled by a local sawmill. The planks were stacked 'in stick' in nearby redundant farm buildings before being processed, graded and installed by a team of Masters degree architecture students from the University of East London. The south-facing fascias to the periscopic balconies have been treated differently, however: both are formed from Medite®Tricoya®Extreme to provide a high-performance, low maintenance solution and a precise edge to the end grain of the cladding on the side walls and to the roof ends above. This, together with the other eco-friendly materials and energy solutions employed, contributed to the Periscope House being the first dwelling in the UK designed to Level 6 of the (no longer extant) Code for Sustainable Homes to secure planning permission through Paragraph 55 of the National Planning Policy Framework (NPPF) which stipulates that only designs of exceptional quality and to the highest architectural standards should be approved for buildings in rural areas, a condition clearly met in the view of the local planning committee who gave the Periscope House its unanimous approval.

Periscope House, Norfolk (2014)
Studio Bark Architects
Photographer: Peter Lander

As mentioned at the outset of this chapter, Accoya® is not the only chemically modified timber product available: Kebony® is a highly durable and dimensionally stable alternative to non-sustainable, imported tropical hardwoods, and a different set of circumstances to those that underpinned the design of the Periscope House prompted its use in a house in Bayswater, one of London's most cosmopolitan areas. The area's streets and garden squares are lined with Victorian brick and stucco terraces and the **The Lateral House** (2013), by Pitman Tozer Architects, is just such a home: set in a conservation area but not listed, the three-storey plus basement villa dates from the 1850s, with an elegant, cream-coloured stuccoed facade that is set back slightly from the street. This outward appearance, however, gives no hint of the radical remodelling that has taken place beyond the front door.

A third storey had been added to the house in the 1970s, lifting it beyond the height of its semi-detached neighbour, but the previous side extension and rear conservatory were considerably less successful and were demolished to be replaced by a new side stair and brick-built outrigger extension to the garden elevation. The transformation of the lower ground level opened up this part of the house to the garden through full height, full width sliding glass doors, immediately outside of which is a deck and seating formed from Kebony®. Steps to the side of this rise through several levels of formal, hard landscaping to arrive at the garden annex. The design of this landscape between the two buildings is extraordinarily controlled and makes it abundantly evident that the interplay between the house and the annex across the garden was an essential consideration in the overall scheme.

**Lateral House,
Bayswater, London** (2013)
Pitman Tower
Photographer: Nick Kane

The effect of this has been to optically draw the garden pavilion closer to the house, the scale and composition of its asymmetrical, timber-clad elevation providing the perfect counterpoint to the rear facade's brick construction. This dark-brown rainscreen of precisely-spaced, open-jointed Kebony® slats rises vertically before following the pitch of the roof to an absolutely horizontal ridge line. The quality of carpentry here is exemplary, as is the detailing: Kebony®'s hardness, workability and low-maintenance credentials are displayed to great advantage in this high-end garden pavilion that multi-tasks as a gym, home office and studio. Inside, the asymmetry of the elevation is followed through with the provision of a small shower/wc, the ply-faced enclosure for which supports a small bed platform below the roof.

Lateral House,
Bayswater, London (2013)
Pitman Tower
Photographer: Nick Kane

Out of the city and back to a corner of England that has already featured in this chapter: this time to the coast of East Sussex at Camber Sands, the county's only sand dunes and a designated Site of Special Scientific Interest (SSSI). The client in this case wished to build a pair of beach houses, the basic brief for each being for open plan living/dining/entertaining spaces and two main and two guest bedrooms. These weekend and summer residences also had to maximise the opportunities offered by the views, but with minimal impact upon the protected landscape environment. Functionally, the buildings needed to be flood resilient, resistant to often hostile marine conditions and be constructed from natural, sustainable materials. All of this to be accommodated in an understated but confident architecture that would sit comfortably alongside existing neighbouring beach houses and the natural backdrop of the changing landscape of the sand dunes and sea.

To firmly anchor the **Beach Houses** (2015) to the site, WAM design opted for heavily insulated (200mm) concrete formwork (ICF) perimeter walls at ground floor level, with exposed beams formed from laminated veneer lumber (Kerto-S LVL by Metsäwood) spanning between the walls and supporting the upper floor and roof structure formed from the same material. The external surfaces of the houses needed to be able to withstand some extreme marine elements in their exposed coastal position. Given this factor, the architects chose Kebony® for the external cladding, in part because of its proven durability when used in harsh climates, but also for its ability to deliver the visual and performance requirements of the design without causing associated environmental degradation—the ultimate benefit anticipated being the silver-grey patina that the Kebony® would develop to echo the natural colours of the dunes and help the buildings blend into the seafront.

In some respects, this was easier said than done: the construction team had to battle sand storms and, to gain access to the site for material deliveries, a temporary corrugated iron road from an adjoining public car park had to be laid across the beach beneath the sand. This limited access to the winter months when the beach was less used by the public, thus ensuring that construction had to be carried out in the worst possible of weathers. The harsh conditions also demanded the use of marine grade stainless steel or powder coated fixings and metalwork throughout. Bravely perhaps, but confident in the cladding product, the architects chose to eschew external gutters and to carefully detail the ridges and eaves to produce a seamless, crisply-finished Kebony® envelope to both houses, decisions vindicated by the numerous awards the buildings have since received, including the East Sussex Heritage Trust Award 2016, the Surface Design Sustainable Award 2016 and the RICS Residential Design Award 2017.

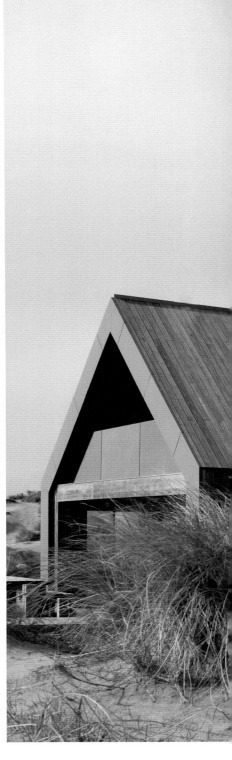

**Beach House,
Camber Sands,
East Sussex** (2015)
WAM Design
Photographer: Stuart Martin

Part 2
Applications

The modern timber house comes in many forms, each having multiple definitions or interpretations: what is meant by 'affordable' housing, for example, and does 'self-build' require home owners to have physically constructed the entire dwelling by themselves? Similarly, home extensions can be large or small; a house can be extensively remodelled or have minor, subtle changes made that prove to be transformational both in the way it is used and also to its external and/or internal appearance. 'Hybrid' too, can describe the use of multiple construction processes or methods, or the combination of a range of products within a particular technological sector, such as timber. The precise characterisation of houses classified as 'suburban' may well include detached or semi-detached homes, bungalows or modern developer-housing projects as well as large individual houses set within reasonably extensive gardens. Others may be categorised as 'regional' in terms of traditional features and materials used or the cultural and environmental context in which they have been built. Greater precision can be afforded to housing that falls within the categories of Passivhaus or 'tall', the former because it has clearly defined standards that prevent the term being used to describe homes that do not meet its demanding energy performance requirements, whilst the latter—in terms of timber structure—nowadays presumes residential developments of six-storeys and above.

Each of these categories of housing provides new possibilities for greater use of timber to be made in their construction. The following chapters explore how doing so can provide an environmentally sustainable response to the current challenges that affect the delivery of increased numbers of house completions in the UK. By way of example, each chapter includes a range of outstanding projects that highlight different ways in which thoughtful—indeed, imaginative—design can bring about significant improvements in the quantity and quality of new homes being built in the UK today. The diversity of houses illustrated here is quite deliberate in this regard: conventional applications of timber frame and panel systems in housebuilding can be found almost anywhere around the country and are largely concealed from sight under an outer skin of brick, stone or render. It is not the purpose of this book to argue which amongst these types of housing developments might be considered as good, bad or indifferent uses of these technologies, particularly as the decision to employ them is more likely to have been based upon economic rather than aesthetic considerations.

That said, not all of the projects featured in the following chapters offer demonstrative visual statements about their timber credentials: some, indeed, are not obvious in the ways in which they make use of timber products and systems but which might well have proved difficult to deliver using other construction methods. Nor have a number of the houses included been delivered at especially low cost: a common misconception about building with timber is that it is a cheap and relatively primitive technology and that it is less durable and less attractive when

Clockhouse Gardens,
Welwyn Garden City (2016)
Stock wool
Photographer: Morley von
Sternberg

85

**Barrett's Grove,
London Borough of Hackney**
(2016)
Groupwork
(formerly Amin Taha Architects)
Photographer: Tim Soar

compared to traditional construction methods. The corollary to this, however, is the fact—as evidenced in this book—that modern timber technologies can deliver very precise, airtight and thermally efficient sustainable homes of extraordinarily high quality. Generally speaking—and due to highly efficient modern methods of offsite manufacture—it is also possible to build more quickly, an important factor when calculating upfront capital expenditure and bank borrowings, onsite plant and equipment costs as well as those incurred in the employment of skilled construction site personnel.

Another point that becomes abundantly clear from the examples highlighted is that modern timber construction is not hidebound by traditional housing models: the design approaches included here show considerable delight in the exploitation of the characteristics and properties of the products and systems available today in order to evolve new—and frequently highly innovative—housing solutions. That all of these have somehow managed to traverse a planning system in the UK that, at times, is accused of being both prejudiced against new or visually different building forms and sclerotic in its decision-making role perhaps indicates the tenacity of the architects, engineers and clients involved in delivering homes of real invention. It also confirms the engagement of individual planning officers in many different parts of the country in helping to evolve a new, timber-based, domestic architecture that is quintessentially of the UK. In this respect, the examples included here of the many ways that timber is nowadays being used in the development of new housing can be seen to be very much part of the country's cultural continuum: or, as Le Corbusier, one of the 20th century's most influential architects, so succinctly put it, *"tradition is nothing but the uninterrupted chain of innovations."*

**Clockhouse Gardens,
Welwyn Garden City** (2016)
Stock wool
Photographer: Morley von Sternberg

Chapter 5
The Affordable Timber House

The provision—or perhaps more accurately, the current deficiency—of affordable housing in the UK has become one of the hot potatoes of our time, a major challenge affecting not only the economic, planning and welfare policies of the government and exercising political minds, as well as those in a wide range of industries including architecture, construction and manufacturing as to the possible solutions that can be delivered at speed. To do so however, requires some clarity as to what 'affordable' actually means when related to housing.

Over the years the term has been subject to multiple interpretations and, according to 'What is Affordable Housing?' (a House of Commons Briefing Paper from November 2016), 'affordable housing' tended historically *"to be interchangeable with references to social housing, i.e. housing developed with an element of government subsidy (grant) and let at sub-market rents by local authorities or housing associations."* This was certainly the case when councils were significant providers of low-rent housing for, by 1980, the proportion of all British housing in state hands was *"large ... by international standards...almost one in three households."* The Housing Act introduced in that same year by Prime Minister Margaret Thatcher radically changed this state of affairs: henceforth, tenants of local authorities were given the 'right to buy' their homes at substantial discounts. The Act envisaged a revolution in how a large section of the British population lived but, whilst this has unquestionably been the case, the impetus underlying it neglected to anticipate any significant population growth (it was presumed at that time to be stable) and the thorny question of what would happen when the UK ran out of cheap housing was one to be addressed another day.

Narford Road,
London Borough of Hackney
(2012)
Fraser Brown MacKenna
Photographer: Tim Crocker

To all intents and purposes, that day arrived some time ago: Shelter estimates there are now 1.4 million households—more than three million people—currently on council house waiting lists, with over 60,000 households in temporary accommodation—a 21% increase since 2010. Five interconnected reasons underlie the huge housing challenge that now exists and the urgent need for more affordable housing to be made available:

1. the UK's population has grown substantially since its 1980s base of 56.31 million to 65,517,525 (as of Saturday, July 8, 2017, based on United Nations estimates): put simply, more homes are required;

2. Demographic changes—we now have more single people and single parent households looking for homes as well as more elderly people looking to downsize from their existing accommodation and there is little flexibility in housing supply to address these altered requirements;

3. housebuilding numbers over this period have been at historic lows and, following the economic crash in 2008, have still to recover to the levels seen before that date;

4. house prices and rents—especially in London, the South East and South West—have risen exponentially, with people on low or average wages priced out of the property purchase and private sector rental markets;

5. under the UK government's austerity programme, wages and salaries in many sectors have been capped since 2010 whilst other costs including property and utility charges have continued to rise.

What then might be done to respond effectively to the urgency of the situation? The UK Government's current definition of 'affordable housing' is *"social rented, affordable rented, and intermediate housing provided to specified eligible households whose needs are not met by the market."* The Scottish Government, by contrast, more broadly interprets it as *"housing of a reasonable (sic) quality that is affordable to people on modest incomes....affordable housing may be in the form of social rented accommodation, mid-market rented accommodation, shared ownership, shared equity, discounted low-cost housing for sale including plots for self-build and low-cost housing without subsidy."* Whilst the UK Government introduced a new Housing Act in 2016 to encourage self- and custom-build housing (see Chapter 6—the Self Build Timber House), this is not primarily focused on affordable housing provision. The Scottish Government, conversely possibly provides more options on how the huge deficit in affordable housing provision might be addressed, but both administrations' definitions are fundamentally focused on matters of tenure and not on how the quality bar for affordable housing might be raised. In this respect, neither can be viewed as especially aspirational: politically, the debate remains all-too grounded in the world of target numbers.

Outside of the UK's parliaments, others have recognised the deficit is not only in the amount of affordable housing that is available, but also in the quality of life offered to residents by many of the homes currently being delivered under this catch-all banner. The following projects demonstrate that other approaches to the provision of affordable housing are possible: approaches where care and consideration at the design stage and in the selection of materials have had a profound and positive impact on the lives of their residents and which have been achieved within the financial constraints currently attached to this category of accommodation.

An overlooked, landlocked plot of land at **Narford Road** (2012) in the Stoke Newington area of the London Borough of Hackney that had formerly been used for light industrial purposes provided the unprepossessing location for an affordable housing development by Fraser Brown MacKenna Architects. The brief from One Housing Group was to maximise the number of high quality, affordable homes that could be fitted onto the awkwardly-shaped site, as well as accommodation for residents with mild learning disabilities. The resulting, timber-framed

Narford Road,
London Borough of Hackney
(2012)
Fraser Brown MacKenna
Photographer: Tim Crocker

scheme is comprised of 44 apartments, plus an 18-bedroom facility that is part of a discrete Care and Support scheme. Designed meet the needs of local people, the 62 homes are a mixture of family housing and single person flats and are organised as four separate buildings, ranging in height from one- to four-storeys and planned to ensure minimum impact on the pre-existing homes that surround the site. Two of these blocks contain the bulk of the apartments and are arranged around two courtyards: Saxony Court is accessed from Geldeston Road to the west and the larger Hazlitt Court is entered from Northwold Road through a brick-built gatehouse that also provides vehicular access for the two wheelchair-accessible apartments in the, otherwise car-free, development. The 18-bedroom care and support facility is entered from Narford Road on the east side of the plot.

The underlying design principle at Narford Road has been to respect and replicate the scale of the existing buildings that surround it and to use materials that are not only warm and tactile, but which also provide an elegant response to site security issues and the need to avoid overlooking and overshadowing of the neighbouring residential gardens. At the higher levels, carefully orientated windows have therefore been employed to prevent overlooking, whilst the lower buildings have been strategically positioned to provide solar and privacy shading.

Narford Road is principally distinguished from other affordable housing projects by the extensive use of vertical timber cladding and screening used on its exterior faces and which effectively unifies the three main blocks into one coherent development. The continuous cladding boards on the main elevations emphasise the project's massing and neatly embrace the dark-grey, aluminium-framed deep-set windows. The screens to the external stair and balconies of the Saxony Court block, in particular, are meticulously detailed, with the boards forming their inside and outside faces fixed back to the concealed metal balustrade on battens that, being visible through the precisely-spaced gaps between the timbers, are horizontally aligned with the cills, frame heads and transoms of the windows.

Superficially, this project may seem quite simple in appearance, but the development at Narford Road is a sophisticated response to an especially challenging brief that demanded affordable housing of high-quality.

Also timber framed and clad, the affordable housing development at **Effra Road** (2012) in the south London district of Brixton, by Inglis Badrashi Loddo Architects has been built on a similar, heavily constrained site to that at Narford Road. Again, the land had formerly been used for light industrial purposes but the dearth of more obvious residential sites in every part of London has pushed the search for plots suited to affordable housing into more difficult brownfield locations that are generally of less interest to large private sector developers. This of course means that the strictly limited budgets in this sector can often struggle to match the cost of dealing with the complex issues presented by difficult ground conditions, party wall agreements and planning stipulations. These, and the fact that many housing associations are precluded by their charters from purchasing sites that do not yet have planning permission in place, can often restrict purchase of these plots to smaller, private sector developers willing to accept the combination of risks involved.

At Effra Road, however, another solution was found to allow construction on the site to be considered. The Kitewood Group, a specialist developer in the delivery of affordable housing in London, bought the land on the basis of a partnership with the London and Quadrant Housing Trust in which the latter would become the ultimate client, with the former bearing the financial risk involved in securing planning permission and other necessary approvals. Two significant planning issues made this process especially fraught, the first being that the London Borough of Lambeth's unitary development plan would only allow a change of use for land that had formerly supported industry if a prescribed period of vacancy had elapsed and only if any housing to be built on the land was 100% affordable. The second issue was no less challenging:

Effra Road, Brixton (2012)
Inglis Badrashi Loddo Architects
Photographer: David Grandorge

that of potential overlooking. Surrounded on three sides by 19th century houses and their gardens, the formal composition of new buildings and the positioning of windows on their rear elevations required a strategy able to successfully address these difficulties.

The answer lay in a housing typology generally referred to as 'the notched terrace', a proposition that, after a successful planning appeal, resulted in the construction of 43 affordable units on the 0.988 acre (0.4 hectare) plot. A narrow access road leads into a small entrance courtyard on the site, from which a left turn takes the visitor into what is effectively a mews lined on both sides with stacked maisonette units. These blocks are made up of a ground floor, three-bedroom flat that open onto their own rear garden, with a two-storey maisonette sits above that is reached by an external stair and entered via a first floor roof terrace. This planning device creates a single-storey, slightly recessed connecting block between the three-storey elements—hence the 'notch'—and the cleverly orchestrated rhythm to what is a high-density, car-free (apart from four disabled spaces) development. Every unit has its own front door and outdoor area or private garden, with the latter mirroring the existing rear gardens on the other side of the site boundary.

From the perspectives of sustainability, construction and budget logic, the Effra Road development makes effective use of timber frame construction and lightweight cladding materials to minimise weight and make it possible to have reduced foundations. The blocks are clad on their mews-side, public facades with vertically-fixed larch boarding with the inner faces of the maisonette elements rendered and painted. Constructed under a Design-Build contract to which the architects were not novated, this is not perhaps as refined in its detailing as other projects to be found in these pages, but given a budget of £1250 sq/m, the architectural solution delivered here to the complex planning scenario presented at the outset highlights the potential not only for notched terraces to deliver high-density, affordable housing in tight, inner-city locations, but also for the economy and flexibility of timber solutions in these situations.

To further illustrate this contention, a very different notched terrace by Peter Barber Architects at **Hannibal Road Gardens** (2012) sits close to the Mile End Road and the Stepney Green Underground station in the London Borough of Tower Hamlets. The project is comprised of of eight large family homes and forms the fourth side of a quadrangle , the other three of which are separate blocks of a post-war social housing estate. The long, narrow site (99 x 7.5m)

Hannibal Gardens, Stepney Green, London (2012)
Peter Barber Architects
Photographer: Morley von Sternberg

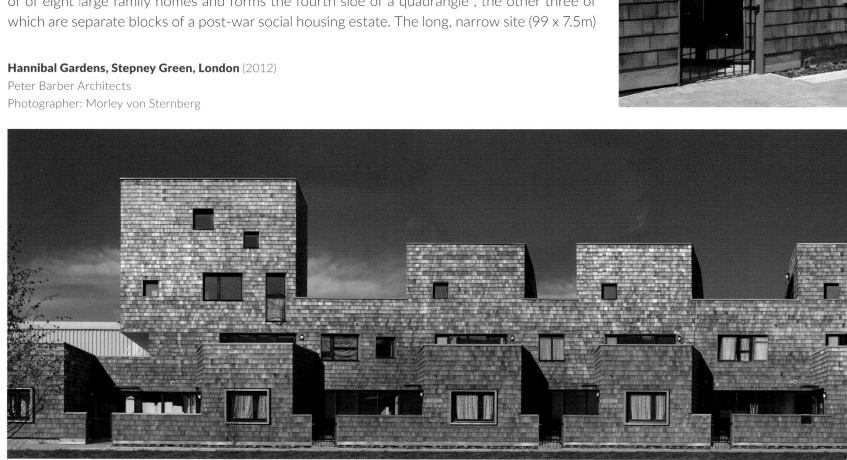

had previously played supporting role to a disused garage and was deemed unsuitable for residential development as it backed onto a zone of industrial buildings, a factor that precluded any proposed building(s) having rear gardens or windows in their back elevations. The existing estate housing, typical of the period, was built cheaply and quickly and with no reference to the surrounding urban context that then existed. Fast forward to more recent times and to the contemporary tenure challenges that are concomitant with multi-generational families living cheek-by-jowl in small apartments in poorer quality, overcrowded buildings.

The Southern Housing Group, one of the largest and oldest housing associations in England, recognised the need for large, three-, four- six- and seven-bedroom socially-rented family dwellings that could cater for all ages and abilities and produced a brief that also required the scheme to meet Lifetime Homes' standards and level 3 of the (no longer extant) Code for Sustainable Homes. The response is a terrace of houses conceived to dignify, soften and humanise the existing buildings, each with its own private, street level entrance courtyard that leads to doors into either the bright and airy living space or the adjacent kitchen/dining area. As prescribed by the planning conditions, the houses, have no windows in their rear facades but, with their notched arrangement, deliver ample daylighting to the first and second floor bedrooms through the glazed screens that open onto the terraces and balconies that look out over the central, communal garden.

The largest of the eight houses sits at the southern end of the development and which, with its additional storey and extended first floor terrace, provides an effective termination point to the formal composition of the terrace. Aside from the three dimensional ingenuity that has been applied in response to the tortuous challenges presented by the site and related regulatory hurdles, these are extraordinarily efficient houses with the absolute minimum of floor space expended on circulation. Indeed, there are none of the corridors, lifts or shared staircases that, normally in this type of development, would account for 20-25% of the building's area and budget.

As seen with the housing at Effra Road, niche terrace solutions can bring many benefits to the development of social housing, including the avoidance of neglected communal spaces and the provision of external areas for residents who otherwise would not have a garden, but it is the ability to use what are effectively low-rise town houses to deliver high-density urban housing that is the real achievement at Hannibal Road Gardens and which makes this terrace/courtyard approach such a strong and convincing model. In itself, this might be regarded by many to be enough, but the most unusual—and certainly the most visually striking—feature of this project is that the entire building envelope has been externally clad with riven western red cedar shingles, a material rarely considered for use in inner city locations. The architects specified what is in fact a very traditional, hand-crafted timber product in reflection of the paraphernalia that occupies the gardens of the existing blocks, but the material has done more than that here: it has brought warmth and texture to the severity of the urban landscape that surrounds it.

Two years on from the three preceding projects to yet another hidden backlands site—this time surrounded by Victorian terraces—and a different tenure model: affordable co-housing. Co-housing is generally defined as an intentional community of private homes clustered around shared space, created and run by their residents. In this model, each attached or single family home has traditional amenities, including a private kitchen. Shared spaces typically feature a common house, which may include a large kitchen and dining area, laundry and recreational spaces. In this example, a group of six families—seven adults and six children—bought a 1000 sq/m plot formerly occupied by a nursery school and commissioned Henley Halebrown Rorrison Architects (HHbR) to design a co-housing project for them.

**Hannibal Gardens,
Stepney Green, London** (2012)
Peter Barber Architects
Photographer: Morley von Sternberg

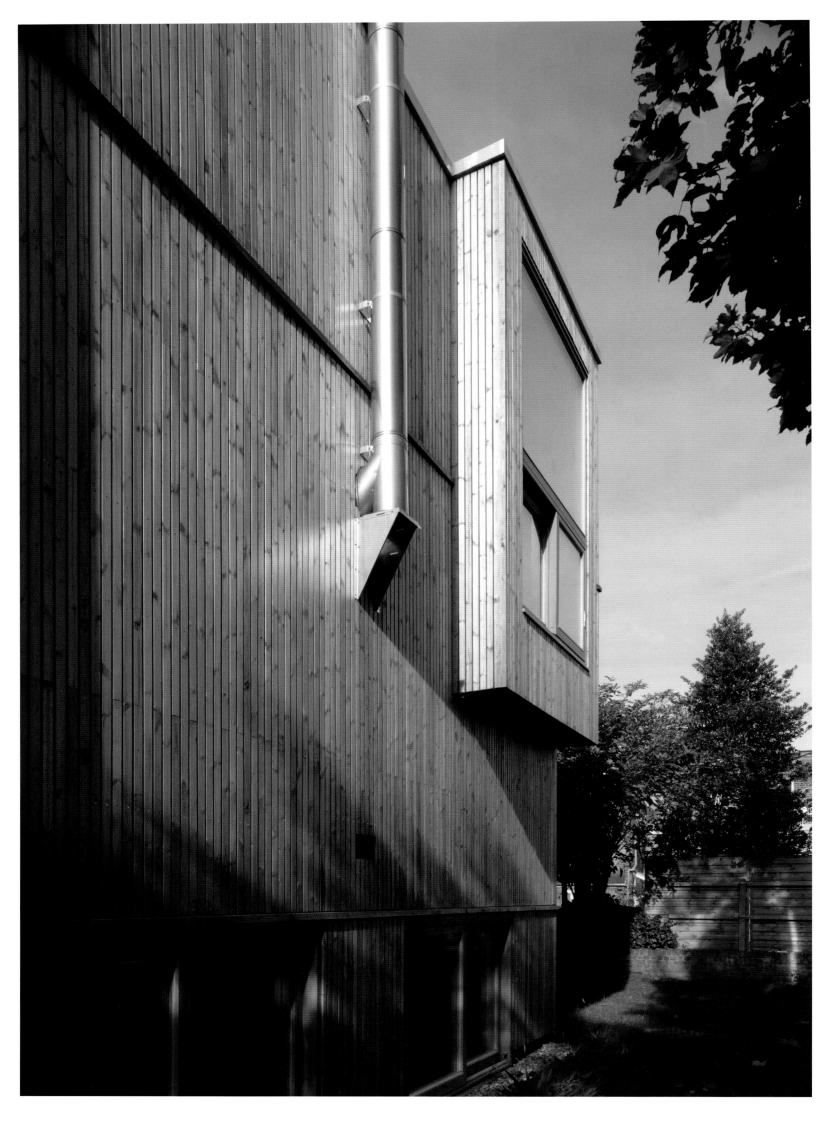

1-6 Copper Lane (2014) in the London Borough of Hackney's Stoke Newington area is the result: London's first co-housing scheme, it is comprised of two rows of three houses, each accessed through a large communal hall at ground floor level and from a shared terrace at first floor level. Clustered around the shared 50 sq/m hall that provides the physical link between the two rows, the six homes range in size from 70-155 sq/m and are designed to Lifetime Homes requirements. The two-storey homes are located in the east and west corners of the development, with the other four houses organised over three floors and arranged in pairs on the north and south corners. Each house interior has been tailored to suit owner requirements, a process that involved intense discussions with the co-housing group members and which in this instance took almost five years to bring the design stage to a conclusion and realise the final construction.

A planning condition intended to minimise the impact of the development on neighbouring houses resulted in the building being dug 1.2m into the ground, the soil condition of which required a light, but stiff, cellular reinforced concrete raft foundation. Above this level, the entire project has been constructed using a lightweight timber frame open panel system filled with mineral wool insulation. The two-storey houses have an outer leaf of Wienerberger bricks; the three-storey houses are clad with ThermoWood® the manufacturing process for which results in a very durable exterior material with a rich, dark brown hue. It is the articulation of this rainscreen, however, that raises this tightly budgeted project above the norm: being sunk into the site, the external perimeter of each house is effectively 2.5 storeys above ground level and, on these faces, the 42 x 42mm ThermoWood® battens have been vertically-fixed at 52mm centres, with the lengths separated at floor levels by a horizontal cill of the same material. The facades to the inner courtyard, by contrast, are divided into two distinct types—below the upper ground floor cill the battens change from square sections to half-parallelograms and continue at the same 52mm centres. Above the cill, at the point where the facades address the raised courtyard, these vertical battens are fixed to 18 x 130mm ThermoWood® boards.

The final result at Copper Lane stands as testimony to the commitment both of the co-housing group members and of the architects who examined many different housing typologies and made several studies aimed at maximising the amount of external communal space within the 950sq/m site. The building itself occupies 795 sq/m but clever planning has not only ensured a triple aspect from each house's living area, it has also created a rich variety of shared garden areas

Copper Lane, Stoke Newington, London (2014)
Henley Halebrown Morrison
Photographer: David Grandorge

around the scheme's perimeter. All this in response to a social need that had arisen through changes in both lifestyle and economics for the group members who, in deciding to follow the co-housing path, made home ownership not only more affordable for themselves but also, with the architects' eloquent use of timber inside and out of the building, have ensured a more congenial and sustainable environment in which to live.

Whilst Copper Lane was a first for London in terms of co-housing, the model is not entirely new, having been around since the 1960s and emerging in the UK in the 1990s. Although being directly involved in the design of a co-housing community and actively contributing to its ongoing development is not necessarily everyone's cup of tea—or indeed one that fits neatly into this country's property financially-driven ownership model—the template has continued to evolve, with projects ranging in size from 10-40 households. One of the most ambitious to emerge in recent years is the Low Impact Living Affordable Community built on the site of an old primary school in the Bramley area of Leeds and designed by Bristol-based White Design. **LILAC** (2013), lays claim to being the UKs first affordable, ecological co-housing project, having been constructed with the Modcell® system that combines timber frame with straw bales and hemp to create super-insulated, prefabricated structural panels finished in lime render and embraced externally by horizontally-fixed western red cedar cladding boards.

As with the Copper Lane scheme, the ambition from the outset at LILAC was to allow individuals and families with shared aims to live together as a community whilst maintaining their own self-contained accommodation. The completed project is comprised of a trio of two-storey and two three-storey blocks that accommodate a mix of one-, two-, three- and four-bedroom homes: 20 units in total, with a sixth 'common house' that contains shared laundry facilities and space where meetings, a weekly shared meal and other communal activities take place. The buildings are grouped in courtyard formation around a central garden area at the south west end of a 1.73 acre (0.7 hectare) plot and have been extremely well integrated with the, now mature, landscape design. The blocks themselves occupy two-thirds of the sloping site, and provide a highly distinctive contrast to the surrounding brick-built, two-storey, semi-detached houses. The obvious evidence of ongoing community engagement clearly shows that the group's confidence not only in the chosen construction method and the resulting building forms but also in the concept of co-housing and the funding model used (the Mutual Home Ownership Scheme) was not misplaced: it has enabled them to secure high quality, affordable accommodation for themselves.

The group's faith in the Modcell® system to deliver the environmental ambitions for the project should not be understated, nor indeed that of the Homes and Communities Agency and the Technology Strategy Board, who assisted the residents in the commissioning of the homes. At a 2013 cost of £3m, this was the first large-scale use of a product conceived to offer, in prefabricated form, an engineered timber frame containing renewable, locally sourced, carbon-sequestering materials. The resulting high-performance, low energy 'passive' buildings (with U-values of 0.19 W per sq/m K) have proved their worth and, with all sides of the political divide now focused on the issue of how to resolve the affordable housing deficit at the same time as dealing with the issue of energy poverty, the time is surely right to investigate how less-than-zero-carbon systems like Modcell® that were once considered innovative, but are now proven, can be rolled out throughout the UK. Unconventional, perhaps, but not everyone holds the same ideas about property ownership and alternative tenure models that eschew the status quo are increasingly demonstrating their capacity to produce housing in which people are not only happy to dwell, but who are simultaneously empowered by the experience.

Chapter 6
The Self-Build Timber House

Unlike in most parts of Europe, the concept of building one's own home has, for many years, been something of an alien concept for people living in large parts of the UK: the construction of new dwellings has instead, and for more than half a century, been dominated by volume housebuilding companies. There are many reasons for this, with difficulties in acquiring land, planning permissions and mortgages being but a few of the obstacles encountered by those wishing to self-build. The numbers electing to take this route and to navigate a passage to a home of their own design or choice have been increasing in recent years, however, stimulated primarily by the increasing un-affordability of new housing, with self-building offering the possibility of a lower cost home than available on the open market. Confidence in doing so has also been encouraged by television programmes, such as Grand Designs, that feature self-builders who have made the journey successfully. This high profile media attention has been supported by a number of specialist magazines and websites that aim to offer inspiration and a degree of hand-holding through the challenges faced by those who have never built before and for whom the first step is to decide which self-build method is most suited to their particular needs, resources and skills.

Traditionally, five self-build approaches have been commonly followed in the UK: the self-built, one-off home approach in which the prospective owner manages the design and construction process as well as undertaking a significant proportion of the actual building work; the contractor built, one-off home approach in which the prospective owner manages the design process and selects a contractor to undertake the construction process; the kit home approach allows the prospective owner to choose a pre-designed house type that the company then erects on the purchaser's behalf; an independent community collaboration in which the prospective owner works with others to acquire a site that is then split into individual plots, before organising the design and construction of his/her own home; and the supported community self-build group approach in which a social landlord or the Community Self-Build Agency helps people to build a group of homes together.

Despite the rising interest in these approaches, the UK still has one of the smallest self-build sectors in Europe—only around 10% of new homes are delivered by this route, with the vast majority of dwellings constructed by the country's 10 largest housebuilding PLCs. Recognising the ever-widening gap between its own targets for new house completions (see Chapter 5—The Affordable Timber House) and the actual numbers constructed by the volume housebuilding sector, the UK Government has relatively recently introduced a number of measures (such as 'Help to Buy') to assist more people to purchase their own home and to facilitate an acceleration in the delivery of greater numbers of houses. As such, the previously undernourished area of self-building has benefited from Government acknowledgement of demand for self-build opportunities and that this has the potential to provide an added, cumulative dimension to

The Hunt House,
Woodseats, Sheffield (2010)
Halliday Clark Architects
Photographer: Camera Crew

housing output that is not dependent upon the availability of large sites and the commercial imperatives of Stock Market listed companies. Thus, a Private Member's Bill—the Self-Build and Custom Housebuilding Act 2015 was passed by Parliament and brought into force in April 2016. This set out to encourage this quietly effective sector to double its output to 20,000 units per year by 2020, a simple piece of legislation complemented by the Government's own Housing and Planning Act 2016 (enacted in July 2016) and a £5 billion Home Building Fund administered by the Homes and Communities Agency. These three initiatives are, in combination, intended to simplify and speed up neighbourhood planning and to unlock brownfield land to provide sites for new homes.

The two Acts also introduced a hybrid model for new house construction—Custom Build, i.e. one that is halfway between classic self-build and traditional development. Increasingly common in parts of Europe such as the Netherlands, Custom Build encourages house buyers to work with a specialist developer to help deliver a semi-bespoke home. In this model, some of the financial and project risks of self-build are offset by a professional team negotiating the building process on the buyer's behalf. This enables consumers to be far more involved in the construction and design of their own homes, but with the direct project management and construction handled by professionals. The conditions attached to Custom Build land supply and finance ostensibly create new opportunities for architects and other housebuilding professionals to participate as development partners in the design and construction of new housing projects comprised of a minimum of 5 units and a maximum of 200 but, at what is still a very early stage in the implementation of this concept in the UK (at the time of writing there are relatively few completed projects), the extent to which Custom Build will make a significant impact on the overall numbers of new homes remains difficult to quantify. Its more immediate value may lie in its capacity to demonstrate a planning and design alternative to the (often cramped) site layouts and house types offered by volume builders.

The Hunt House, Woodseats, Sheffield (2010)
Halliday Clark Architects
Photographer: Camera Crew

What is not in doubt is the range of possibilities the approach offers for greater use of timber products and construction systems in the delivery of significant numbers of new homes: the combination of offsite manufacture, speed of erection, build quality, enhanced airtightness and thermal performance, as well as considerable design flexibility, is likely to see timber construction's share of the UK housebuilding market rise substantially from its current level of 20% of new-build completions.

As an indicative measure of its potential in this new area, the use of timber in its many forms is already the preferred method of construction for many self-builders, with a wide variety of different systems—timber frame, open and closed panels and structural insulated panels (SIPs)—being used. There is also increasing interest in building with solid timber products such as cross- and dowel-laminated panels as well as laminated veneer lumber (LVL). Many, however, have opted for SIPS as their first choice, the product offering, to all intents and purposes, a 'flat pack' home in which the insulation and structure are effectively part of the same, relatively thin, wall and thus freeing up more usable space within—an attractive feature when the plot area is small. A good example is the three-storey **Hunt House** (2010) in Sheffield's Hackthorn Road, by Halliday Clark Architects, a project that makes a virtue of its location and its diminutive footprint, particularly as a self-build, timber-based home is not usually the first option to come to mind when considering ways to terminate a stepping, two-storey brick-built Victorian terrace.

Located to one side of the end-terrace property which the clients had purchased in 2007, the driveway was originally the site of two other terraced houses that had been condemned and demolished in the 1970s but, with a burgeoning home business prompting the need for larger, dedicated premises capable of being built within a very tight budget, its proximity was ideal for this eco-friendly, self-build house. The planning application for the three-bedroom dwelling with home office was submitted towards the end of 2009 and, once approved under Delegated Powers, was completed and occupied within a year, a testament to the efficacy of the SIPs method of construction. In this instance, the Kingspan Tek Building System was used, with a builder employed to carry out the construction work.

The design of the Hunt House's front elevation takes its cue from the established street geometry, replicating the width of a single terrace unit (but not its Victorian architecture) and leaving space to the side for a new driveway. Excavating into the sloping rear garden made intelligent use of the site's tight footprint since it not only allowed the house to be set back from the terrace's long facade and aligned in height with the ridge of the adjacent roof, but also enabled the introduction of an external yard/bike store to the rear. Extending the Siberian larch clad house backwards in this way had the additional benefit of increasing its outdoor areas through the creation of a roof garden and balconies. Internally, the high levels of airtightness and thermal efficiency inherent in the structural insulated panels, together with a mechanical ventilation and heat recovery (MVHR) system, have meant that the property has rarely required more heating than that provided by the very efficient wood-burning stove in the main living space. An unusual and highly original end-of-terrace exemplar solution that was built to Level 4 of the (no-longer-extant) Code for Sustainable Homes, the Hunt House won the Self-Build category of the Telegraph Homebuilding and Renovating Magazine Awards in 2011.

A quite different illustration of the use of SIPs, **Sandpath** (2014), by Adrian James Architects, has to be one of the simplest, least expensive, high quality self-build timber houses to be found anywhere but, as with any new construction on a previously occupied site (the house replaced a run-down bungalow), a number of challenges had to be overcome in the course of developing a satisfactory design solution.

The five-bedroom house is located in Beckley, a small village a few miles north of Oxford and within the city's Green Belt. Planning permission already existed for a three-bed chalet-

Sandpath, Beckley, Oxfordshire (2014)
Adrian James Architects
Photographer: Adrian James Architects

bungalow on the plot, but the client-builder wished to increase the amount of liveable space and to construct a rather different style of house. To do so required a design that, whilst conforming to Green Belt restrictions on height (no higher than the neighbouring house) and plan area (the new footprint could be no larger than that of the previous dilapidated house), would push these to their absolute limits. In addition, the plot had a distinct slope from one side to the other, a characteristic from which advantage has been taken in two ways: first to integrate a basement level within the house, and second to level out the rear garden and forecourt to meet the ground floor plane. These external areas are contained by a concrete dwarf wall, over which one end elevation of the house has been cantilevered a short distance forward, creating a more dynamic, three-dimensional appearance.

As ever with self-build projects, budget limitations demand economic design decisions and, at Sandpath, a combination of pragmatism and spatial awareness has been employed to considerable effect. The existence of an overhead power line, and the excavation equipment's inability to access the site from the lower driveway level, made digging out the basement a more difficult process but, once completed and its structure tanked, an economically and thermally-efficient flatpack structural insulated panel (SIPs) system was used to form the house's simple volume. An airtight membrane was introduced within the SIPs envelope to increase the energy efficiency of the completed house and this, combined with a mechanical ventilation heat recovery (MVHR) system and a proprietary air source heat pump hot water system, have ensured low energy bills.

Sandpath is capped with a flat roof rather than the pitched option favoured by its neighbours, a common compositional and constructional device that has allowed the internal volume to be filled with occupied space up to the building's full allowable height. The timber structural system has also facilitated the ground floor's open-plan arrangement, with the only visible concession to other materials being a seemingly weightless, folded metal staircase behind a glass screen which, together, form the central focus of the kitchen/dining/living area.

Externally, the house walls are clad with horizontally-fixed, untreated Western Red Cedar boards, a tried and tested homogeneous solution that here emphasises the house's rectilinear appearance. In contrast, the composite timber and aluminium windows are painted green, a subtlety that lifts the design above comparisons with the agricultural vernacular of the area. As an example of how to do simple things well, Sandpath amply demonstrates how a great deal can be achieved by self-builders on a tight budget when the starting points have been carefully thought through and the design developed to deliver a solution that is economical in terms of capital, maintenance and running costs. The result of a strong relationship between architect and client, Sandpath is an understated, yet elegant, self-build house of considerable quality: in other words, a real success—so much so that the architects and other members of the construction team have now formed a separate company to market the multi-award-winning concept in 2-, 3- and 4-bedroom kit-form units—replacing the SIP elements with cross laminated timber—as the 'Kiss ('keep it simple, stupid') House'. In the new, Government-encouraged world of self-build, this may well prove an attractive, affordable option for many self-builders.

A self-build property that can hardly be portrayed as an overt demonstration of the use of timber in its design and construction but which, nevertheless, is an excellent example of a panelised timber system approach, is the four-bedroom **Tree House** (2014) by McChesney Architects. Tucked off Sydenham Park Road in the South East London Borough of Lewisham, the house sits within the Sydenham Park Conservation Area and overlooks Albion Millennium Green, one of 245 Millennium Greens created across the UK in 2000 as protected areas of green space intended to provide "permanent breathing spaces" and "places of tranquility" in urban areas. The client had purchased a Victorian house with a large garden with potential to partition off part of it to create a plot for a new dwelling. It, together with the surrounding villas, was a characteristic fin de siècle confection of shapes and forms—an architectural context the Council's planning department was anxious that any new proposal should avoid attempting to pastiche. The design approach taken in response was to create something completely new: in the architect's words "a simple crisp form, honed in its detail". Despite a local campaign of opposition, the planning committee approved the application at its first hearing, at which stage the architect's appointment was concluded, this having always been intended as a self-build project for which the client would manage the works and appoint sub-contractors himself. With this in mind, the architect had detailed many of the critical facade junctions to ensure the original design intent, as approved, would be faithfully realised.

Redberry Grove, Sydenham (2014)
Ian McChesney Architects
Photographer: Adam Scott, Ian McChesney

Sliding House, Suffolk (2009)
dRMM Architects
Photographer: Alex de Rijke

The form of the house comprises two volumes: one, a long slim enclosure containing the circulation and service areas with entrances from both the Albion Villas Road and Redberry Grove ends of the site; the other a longer rectangular volume containing the body of the house, the conjoined elements topped with a butterfly roof that pitches down from its highest points on the west and east elevations to the long valley between. The house is set out lengthwise on a precise, 1500 mm grid, the narrower end facades using a 1600 mm module for the main block and a 2000 mm width for the staircase enclosure; overall, an arrangement well suited to the use of a panel system. In this instance, prefabricated Scandia-Hus panels, closed and insulated on one side and open on the other, were employed, the remaining empty volume in the panel frame, together with the cavity behind the rainscreen cladding, was filled on site with a further thickness of insulation, thereby obviating any cold bridge issues.

Three sides of the house's raised ground floor living area are glazed to full room height with Iroko-framed, triple glazed panels, the grid of which is matched by the flush, opaque black glass, open-jointed rainscreen cladding system, that covers the remainder of the house's exterior. Deep, Iroko-framed reveals to the first floor bedroom windows (all of which look into the adjacent Green) evidence the thickness of the heavily insulated panel walls that, together with an underfloor heating system throughout and a wood burning stove centred in the open-plan living area, enabled the house to achieve Level Four of the (no longer extant) Code for Sustainable Homes and—considered by many to be even more important for a self-build property—a full ten-year NHBC warranty. Internally, a beautifully detailed and manufactured oak stair is lit from above by clerestory windows and frameless skylights that occupy four grid bays. Far from being a conventional timber-based project, No.5 Redberry Grove clearly shows that a decision to utilise an offsite manufactured timber system need not preclude or inhibit genuinely creative and quality-driven design.

An earlier, but still one of the most individual—and adventurous—self-build timber homes to be found in the UK today is the **Sliding House** (2009) by London-based architects, dRMM. Situated in Suffolk on a smallholding previously occupied by a bungalow, outbuildings and a caravan, this seemingly inauspicious location was nevertheless subject to stringent local planning requirements for rural developments. Taking its design inspiration from the timber-framed and clad 'shed' tradition of the area's vernacular farm buildings, the architects, in addressing the maximum height and width prescribed for new dwellings, succeeded in introducing a degree of innovation seldom seen in domestic, self-build projects. In this they had the happy acquiescence of their client, a mathematician and motor bike enthusiast who was well able to assess the financial and other risks inherent in the mechanics of this radical design proposition. That he also had the skills to carry out his own cost control, manage the various sub-contracted packages and undertake a degree of the building work himself in association with the various local and specialist contractors is testament to the high levels of performance and quality achievable within the wide parameters of the 'self-build' appellation.

The house is arranged in linear form along a level, north-south oriented ridge, with the 28-metre long structure made up of three distinct parts: the 16-metre house, a seven-metre annexe and a five-metre garage. The latter, set between the house and annexe, has been shifted onto a parallel axis to create a courtyard between the project's principal elements.

Each of these component parts is distinguished by the use of different materials and colours—red rubber membrane, glass and red/black stained larch cladding. The bedroom/service part of the main house is constructed from modular timber cassettes (closed panels), whilst the ground and first floor levels of the living area are housed within a curtain wall glazing system. The glazed structure is separated at the upper gallery level from the first floor bedroom area by a roof terrace that contains a bathroom that is open to the elements. The annexe and garage are also formed from modular timber cassettes.

All of this (aside, perhaps, from the external bath) may seem quite conventional but it is the element that unites the house's three parts that makes it unique: a 20-tonne mobile roof and wall system constructed from steel (frame), timber, insulation and a larch rain screen. This independent carapace is able to glide along hidden tracks in the concrete raft to provide a

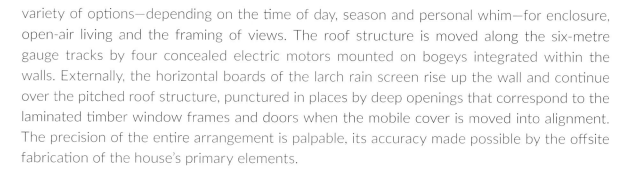

**Little Lindisfarne, nr. Hawick,
Scottish Borders** (2015)
Brian Robertson
Photographer: Nigel Rigden

variety of options—depending on the time of day, season and personal whim—for enclosure, open-air living and the framing of views. The roof structure is moved along the six-metre gauge tracks by four concealed electric motors mounted on bogeys integrated within the walls. Externally, the horizontal boards of the larch rain screen rise up the wall and continue over the pitched roof structure, punctured in places by deep openings that correspond to the laminated timber window frames and doors when the mobile cover is moved into alignment. The precision of the entire arrangement is palpable, its accuracy made possible by the offsite fabrication of the house's primary elements.

To many, the level of elaboration involved in the Sliding House's design and construction may seem an unnecessary affectation, but in environmental and practical terms the solution arrived at answers a number of common questions: the living area is, *de facto*, a very large conservatory that provides natural thermal comfort, the levels of which can be controlled by moving the position of the roof. Equally, the roof is able to deliver shade and cooling when required, the only mechanical support necessary for year-round operation being a ground source heat pump to give additional warmth during especially cold periods. This, ultimately, is a cleverly planned two-bedroom home with a one-bed annexe and garage that has effectively rewritten the rules for the level of ambition achievable in the design of self-build houses in rural areas.

In each of the foregoing examples, the architect has brought a valuable, added dimension to the process, irrespective of which of the five self-build routes explained earlier has been followed by the client/house owner. **Little Lindisfarne** (2015), near Hawick in the Scottish Borders is, however, largely the work of the owner and his wife, who drove the project through two years of architectural, engineering, planning, site and utility obstacles to produce an extremely well-resolved, almost wholly timber home that is a model of environmental and social sustainability. Having parted with not one, but two, architects for reasons associated with substantial departures from the brief and consequent budget over-runs, the client then discovered the advice he had been given as to the suitability of building a long, slim timber-framed house with substantial cantilevers on the sloping site had omitted to take into account the likely windsail effect of the prevailing west wind, a pressure that, in this situation, required the rigidity of structural steel portal frames. In addition, the implications of the detailed topographical survey had been missed and, with the datum point in the wrong place on the original design drawings, a lot more excavation was required than previously anticipated.

The house's proposed appearance too, failed to find favour with the Borders Council planning department which described it as 'brutal and boxlike' but, with no part of the design actually contravening policy or regulation, permission to build was eventually secured. Paradoxically, the house was subsequently commended in the Council's own Design Competition 2016 and, it would be only fair to mention that the Local Authority has become much more aware of the potential value of the extensive forest resource in its own area and the need to support the design of buildings that reflect the benefits and qualities of timber construction.

So much for the problems: determined to maintain their commitment to environmental and social responsibility in the construction of their house, the owners' strategy was to appoint tradespeople and secure materials and building components from within the vicinity of Hawick or, if this wasn't possible, from the wider Borders area and failing this, from companies based in Scotland, all with the intention of supporting employment and keeping the spend within the local or regional economies. On this basis, the couple appointed a Hawick-based contractor, blacksmith, plasterers and electricians as well as a local engineer to take the project through the Scottish Building Control process to secure the necessary Building Warrant. The owner himself took on the role of builder's labourer and joiner's mate throughout the construction period. Major components such as external timber, flooring and windows were found further afield and, with the locally available larch deemed to be insufficiently dense compared to the Scotlarch® cladding produced by Russwood, a well-know and highly respected timber supplier, the cladding fell into the owners' 'wider Scotland' procurement band, coming from Newtonmore, near Inverness. Similarly, the large patio doors and windows were procured even further north, from Dornoch-based Treecraft.

In terms of its design, Little Lindisfarne has clearly taken its cue from the work of Peter Womersley (1923-93) the architect of several important modern buildings in the Borders including, in particular, the studio (1958) at High Sunderland, near Selkirk, for Bernat Klein, the renowned textile designer. In layout, the house is nestled into the sloping site and arranged on two levels with open-plan spaces inside. A series of steel portal frames is set at intervals along its length and infilled between with open panel frames stick-built on site and heavily insulated between the studs. Externally, the house is clad entirely with the aforementioned Scotlarch®, installed vertically, board-on-board. One long elevation is unpunctuated by windows, whilst the other has two extended horizontal bands of narrower cladding boards, with windows to bedrooms, bathrooms and living areas on each floor interrupting this linear arrangement where required. The end result is a simple, elegant house, the appearance of which belies its troubled beginnings, but which also further demonstrates the resilience of timber construction when used in the delivery of high quality, self-build homes. With more attention now on the potential of this sector to help ease the country's chronic housing shortage, houses like those highlighted here not only offer many lessons to the uninitiated, but invariably have owners who are willing to share their knowledge and experience of how to overcome pitfalls.

From this perspective, the UK could, over the next few years, witness the emergence of a new generation of context-specific, individual homes with outstanding environmental credentials. Further, the prospect of the energy, imagination and tenacity involved being also reflected at larger scale in the conception and development of Custom Build housing projects is an enticing one: the wider architectural profession is arguably only just beginning to recognise and engage with this. When the first, larger-scale results begin to appear around the country and the lessons from the first, pioneering tranche of Custom Build housing projects are duly disseminated, the sector could well find itself in a position to lead a radical transformation in the methods conventionally used to deliver new homes in the UK. The ongoing development of new, more efficient and environmentally responsible timber technologies has the potential to provide invaluable underpinning to the culture shift necessary to build significant numbers of high quality houses at speed.

Little Lindisfarne, nr. Hawick, Scottish Borders (2015)
Brian Robertson
Photographer: Nigel Rigden

Chapter 7
The Remodelled Timber House

The term 'adaptive re-use' has been current in architectural circles for at least two decades and is usually associated with the regeneration of a historic building or landscape, but it also refers to the process of reusing an old site or building for a purpose other than for which it was built or designed. Along with brownfield reclamation, adaptive re-use is seen by many as a key factor in land conservation and the reduction of urban sprawl. After built structures become disused or abandoned, adaptive re-use has the potential to breathe new life into an old building, while conserving resources as well historic and community value. There are many aspects to this area of work: economic, social and environmental as well as conservation, preservation and sustainability, all of which manifest themselves in a different order of priority in each project. One constant pervades many of the buildings reviewed in this category: the innovative use of timber as a means of ensuring a building's future life.

There can be few more obvious examples of adaptive re-use than the transformation of a dilapidated outbuilding, formerly a chicken shed, into a contemporary dwelling. **The Shed**, by David Grindley Architects, is in Bow Brickhill, a village south-east of Milton Keynes, and forms the boundary to a Victorian primary school and sits within the curtilage of a Grade II listed farmhouse. Although the 19th century building was not in a Conservation Area, planning permission was required to change its use from agricultural to residential and also for the substantial external works proposed around it as the, once agrarian, but long-neglected, landscape is located within an Area of Attractive Landscape (AAL), a designation particular to Buckinghamshire. The subsequent permission established a framework intended to secure the tract's long-term future and included gardens and stepped terraces, around which planting could develop and change. The 154 sq/m house flanks an existing pond that was enlarged as part of the external works and this approach to retention and re-use permeates the design and construction philosophy applied to the project by its architects. Working with the existing building footprint, the over-riding environmental strategy was to produce a well-insulated envelope and to minimise fabrication and construction waste Many of the existing materials found on the site were re-used, including roof slates, plinth bricks, stone boulders and the 19th century roof trusses that are now exposed to provide visual evidence that this modern home has a pedigree. These timber king post trusses, with their coarse-textured patina of age derived from originally having been hewn and assembled by hand, provide a noble counterpoint to the house's crisp, contemporary finishes.

Externally, the shed is best seen from across the pond and where the strategy applied, wherever new materials were to be used, was that they should natural, durable, self-coloured of low embodied energy is most evident. The main body of the long single-storey building is roofed with natural slates. The east, timber-framed, elevation below it is clad along its full length with horizontally-fixed oak boards that are punctuated by four, storey-high, folding shutters formed

El Ray, Dungeness (2010)
Simon Conder Architects
Photographer: Paul Smoothy

from the same material and which provide security to the full height windows and doors behind. At each end of this central block, the gables are extended as if having been slid out from within the roof and walls: that to the north is longer and contains a separate office space, whilst the one to the south frames large gazed doors that open out from the living area onto an extensive terrace. In delivering such a carefully considered, sustainable design solution, the architects of the Shed have also ably demonstrated that functional obsolescence does not need to mean the end of a building's useful life.

Nor should it mean the end of an artefact's existence, no matter how idiosyncratic it may seem. At Dungeness, on the Kent Coast, the shingle beach has long been the site of an extraordinary range of detritus assembled into huts and holiday cabins. Nowadays, this paraphernalia is considered to be very much part of the Dungeness *genius loci*—so much so, in fact, that the local planning department insists on the retention of this material when any new structure is proposed in replacement. The range of unusual objects that have found their way to this particular beach is wide and occasionally surreal, one such being a 19th century railway carriage. Quite how it found its way onto Dungeness beach is possibly a whole other story, but the most recent chapter in its long existence began when the eponymous principal of Simon Conder Architects inherited it and the shack-like structure it was encased in.

As described elsewhere in this book (Chapter 2—The Framed and Panelled Timber House), the beach at Dungeness has, over recent years, developed into what might best be described as an informal architectural research and development park, particularly in the use of timber, a material that, through its historical application in the construction of fishermen's huts in this location, has effectively become synonymous with this flat, exposed landscape.

With its project for **El Ray** (2010), Simon Conder Architects grasped the opportunity to further the practice's own experience in the creative the use of timber. The building's bell-shaped plan has been formed around the railway carriage that, scrubbed and cleaned, but with its weathered

The Shed,
Bow Brickhill, nr. Milton Keynes,
Buckinghamshire (2012)
David Grindley Architects
Photographer: David Grindley
Architects

paintwork left untouched, has been adapted and re-used as the kitchen in the redesigned and rebuilt weekend and holiday dwelling. Comprised of two bedrooms, a bathroom and a living area, the building is unconventionally entered via a long, boarded walkway that crosses the beach to a door set centrally in the 'domed' end of the 'bell' and into a passage that leads between the two sleeping areas. Beyond this, centred on the house's long axis, is the carriage/kitchen sitting proudly in the middle of the open plan living area. Here the curved walls splay out to frame the view to the sea, with the full-width, sliding glass doors set back to within the structure that provides shelter to the outside deck.

The construction of this remarkable building is heavily insulated, the material set between 200mm deep I-joists used vertically as the studs in a single-storey timber frame that is braced with OSB. Above, the imperceptible slope of the roof (a 2° incline, in response to planners' demand that it be pitched) is supported on MetsäWood's Kerto laminated veneer lumber (LVL) beams. Externally, the vertical cladding and decking have been formed from louro itauba, a hardwearing and weather resistant FSC-certified hardwood. In other circumstances, El Ray would be considered an unusual dwelling: at Dungeness it fits perfectly within the beach's unique genre of adapted and reused artefacts.

At the other end of the country, Tiree is the most westerly island of Scotland's Inner Hebrides: between it and Canada there is only ocean. Its only association with Dungeness rests on the fact that it is also flat and treeless for, unlike the shingled Kent shore, Tiree is edged with long, sandy beaches. The traditional dwelling form here, as on other Hebridean islands (see Chapter 10—The Regional Timber House), is the Black House, a low, single-storey structure

El Ray, Dungeness (2010)
Simon Conder Architects
Photographer: Paul Smoothy

with thick, white-painted walls built from local rubble and with a steeply-pitched turf or thatch roof to shelter its residents from the harsh environment outside. Nowadays, the island's 7834 hectares of machair landscape is sparsely populated (the most recent census in 2011 registered 653 inhabitants) and the ruins of former dwellings stand as mute criticism of slow decline. Some of these structures are considered to be of sufficient historical merit to justify listing by Historic Environment Scotland, one such being **House No.7** (2013), the black house rebuilt and extended for his parents by the principal of Denizen Works. The practice, established two years before the completion of the project, is set up as "a collaborative studio to develop projects of different scales that are founded on an understanding of place." Its stated approach is "a desire to create work that taps into local history, landscape, culture and microclimate."

The rebuilt and extended project has three constituent parts: the ruined black house has been converted to a guest suite containing two bedrooms, a bathroom and a snug within the two-storeys that now sit beneath its steeply sloped and black-tarred roof; the barrel-vaulted 'Livinghouse' containing the dwelling's living, dining and kitchen areas; and the utility block that houses a utility room, a wet room for coats and boots and a small studio space. The Livinghouse and the utility block are linked to form an L-shape that wraps around one end of the rebuilt black house and provide shelter to a small garden that has been created to the rear. A top-lit passageway connects the three quite different built elements, the design and construction of which have, on the one hand, been grounded in careful analysis of the vernacular buildings of Scotland's Highlands and Islands and, on the other, the practicalities of construction in remoter areas. In the case of treeless Tiree, the prospect of gales is a fundamental consideration, with House No.7's timber frames having to be engineered to withstand a horizontal wind loading of 1.44 KN per sq/m. Supply of building materials and components was also constrained by what could be shipped to the island aboard a CalMac ferry and, with the structures of both the Livinghouse and the utility block formed from curved glulam portal frames CNC machine-tailored for the project, the design had to accommodate these being fabricated and assembled in easily transported sections.

House No.7, Isle of Tiree, Inner Hebrides (2013)

Denizen Works

Photographer: David Barbour

The roofs to the Livinghouse and the utility block are clad with sinusoidal galvanised steel sheets—'wrinkly tin', in the local vernacular—with the gable ends to the Livinghouse clad with wide (150 x 22mm), tar-painted Scottish larch planks, installed vertically and fixed board-on-board. The stone walls of the black house guest suite have been lined with an insulated timber frame, whilst the roof above was constructed using traditional timber frame methods and topped with a curved ridge formed from profiled timbers. Pine tongue-and-groove boards—a traditional material in this part of the world—are evident throughout the interiors, the pièce-de-résistance being the church-like barrel-vaulted ceiling to the living/dining/kitchen area of the Living House. A masterly example of adaptive re-use, House No.7 is the built manifestation of the Denizen Works agenda highlighted earlier; it is an example of adaptive re-use so successful that it justifiably received a plethora of prestigious architectural awards including Grand Designs' 'House of the Year' in 2014.

The black house typology does of course date back several hundred years and its cultural status is well understood, but one of the more peculiar features of the modern constructed world is a general reluctance to value the mainstream of buildings from the 20th century when their original use has come to an end or their technical infrastructure is deemed to be obsolete. There is rarely the same groundswell of opinion demanding their preservation as there is for properties deemed to be older and, by extension, more historically important. Yet, when confronted with the economic, environmental and social issues associated with a building's demolition, a different response can often emerge, based on the simple understanding that the construction of a new building will generally have a greater embodied energy cost than if the existing structure were to be adaptively reused. There may also be recognition of wider sustainability issues insofar as they affect the existing community: the possibility of negative change to the landscape of the local built environment; the break in continuity with the past; the potential loss of local identity and amenity; and the consequential reduction in community size and economic stability.

Quite often, however, an existing building may be considered of negligible architectural worth and, in the case of A449 Architects' design for **Blakeburn Cottage** (2015), near Melrose in the Scottish Borders, the starting point for renovation and extension was a characterless 1970s bungalow. The post-war period saw many of Scotland's rural areas scarred with nondescript bungalows and ill-proportioned kit houses (a topic more fully addressed in Chapter 10—The Regional Timber House), with neither typology built with much, if any, concern for their impact on the country's rich diversity of landscapes, architectural traditions and local cultures. Yet, it may be that the fundamental construction of many of these buildings remains relatively sound and, in a world increasingly aware of the benefits to be had from the application of Circular Economy principles, the question arises of how much, rather than how little, of the existing fabric can be repurposed through the application of some creative design thinking. With demolition and construction of a new-build often a stumbling block with planners, the philosophy applied at Blakeburn Cottage has been to retain as much of the existing fabric as possible: a decision, the architect contends, that allowed construction to move more quickly and that the process was cost-neutral relative to any VAT saving made through compete demolition. Here, the house has all the appearance of being entirely new,

**Blakeburn Cottage,
nr. Melrose,
Roxburghshire,
Scottish Borders** (2015)

A449 Architects
Photographer: David Barbour

125

Ansty Plum, Wiltshire (2015)
Coppin Dockyard
Photographer: Brotherton Lock

but closer inspection reveals the palimpsest of the bungalow's footprint, whilst the form of the gable ends has been driven by the profile of the host structure. Concrete chimney stacks also nod to the scale of the original building, with other alterations and additions subtly introduced: the old building underwent a full, internal strip-out to create more flexible space; the plan was lengthened at both ends; and ceilings removed and the roof opened up to provide double height space to every room. The characteristics that give the impression that this house is new, however, are the taut-detailing of vertically-fixed larch rainscreen and the fine edge to the eaves of the slate-clad roof, features emphasised by the concealment of gutters and downpipes. Blakeburn appears as a minimal, modern home, its antecedent given unexpected new life, form and continuity.

The same might be said for **Ansty Plum** (2015), in the small south-west Wiltshire village of Ansty, by the Coppin Dockray Architecture and Design Studio, except that the 20th century architecture credentials in this case are considerable. The house was designed in 1964 by David Levitt, a founding partner of the renowned practice, Levitt Bernstein, for one of Ove Arup's former partners and has an adjacent studio by architectural luminaries, Alison and Peter Smithson. Its location is no less daunting: set on a steeply sloping site, the house overlooks a group of 12th century buildings but, these attributes notwithstanding, the house had fallen into disrepair and, because it was built at a time when heating with fossil fuels was less understood— or expensive—than today, the extensively-glazed building structure and steeply inclined roof were virtually uninsulated. How then to insulate and heat this architecturally-significant house without undermining the clarity of the buildings form and materials? The architects' role here required experience and considerable sensitivity in first stripping out layers of additions accumulated over the years to expose the original form of the building. The original open plan internal layout was re-formed to accommodate a new kitchen, study and bedroom, with bespoke furniture, new joinery and floor finishes added. Much of the work carried out remains unseen: a process of stitching and mending wherever required: new windows, heating, lighting, an air source heat pump, as well as high levels of thermal insulation have been imperceptibly introduced in order to bring the house up to 21st century standards and reduce its carbon emissions by 80%. Adaptive re-use here has also re-established Ansty Plum as something of an icon amongst the UK's more understated 20th century timber houses.

**Highbury Terrace Mews,
Highbury,
London Borough of Islington**
(2013)

Studio 54 Architecture
Photographer: Sarah Blee

Away from the country, what began as a modest commission to upgrade insulation and add a shower room to a two-storey house at **17A Highbury Terrace Mews** (2013) in the London Borough of Islington, gradually metamorphosed into a much larger job for Studio 54 Architecture that involved the complete redesign of the building's front elevation and the fit-out of several key internal spaces. The property boom of the early 1980s had led to some gentrification in the Highbury area and the original building was constructed in 1988 as part of a row of six dwellings conceived in an eclectic mixture of styles and detailing that would normally defy categorisation but which, at that time, was fashionably promoted under the term, 'postmodern classicism'. Making significant alterations to the exterior of only one house in the row proved to be a difficult negotiation with the local authority's planning department, however, resulting in a time-consuming process that was ultimately resolved with the scheme being finally accepted without compromise.

Other houses in the terrace have strange, rounded dormer windows rising above the common cornice line. The intention at No.17a was to rationalise and simplify the front elevation by replacing its windows, altering the roofline and unifying the whole with new external cladding above the ground floor. Visually, the house exterior has been dramatically changed: the exposed brickwork at street level now washed with grey paint, whilst above, varying widths of black-stained Douglas fir boards have been hung vertically, with the slightly projecting central part of the elevation rising to meet the height of dormers further along the terrace. The existing window openings at first floor level were retained within this new facade and two new ones inserted to light the room in the roof above. Those windows that are fixed have been set flush and the openable ones set back; the latter, internally, have deep reveals lined with oiled cedar panelling. Although a relatively small remodelling project, the decision to give the building an entirely new timber skin has effected a clear and qualitative distinction between it and the architectural mediocrity of the properties it neighbours onto.

Elsewhere in London, the earlier remodelling of an existing, double-fronted Edwardian house in Clapton was very much the reverse of the work carried out at Highbury Mews: the existing street facade of the property at **Atherden Road** (2010) was retained, but almost everything behind it changed. The alterations carried out were far from wilful, however, but instead a necessary response to structural investigations that revealed the extensive damage the house had suffered from a bomb that fell nearby during World War II and which had not been properly repaired. As a consequence, the original proposal by Hugh Strange Architects required significant revision. The clients' brief at the outset was to add an additional bedroom and bathroom to their two-storey, two-bedroom house, but an initial feasibility study indicated that relocating the sleeping areas to the ground floor and moving the living/dining/kitchen upstairs, could provide two more bedrooms, with the additional benefit of more natural light for the living spaces. The surprise news of the bomb damage also came with an expensive, 65-year-old aftershock: having reconsidered what parts of the build fabric could be retained, the decision was made to reconstruct the roof, the upper floors and the entire rear elevation. Only the street facade and the front two rooms of the ground floor were retained, whilst still working within the existing party walls.

The resulting remodelling of the house can only be described as inspired in its design conception, the selection of materials and the detailing, all of which had to take cognisance of the clients', by that stage, very overstretched budget. Off-the-shelf timber trusses and inexpensive plywood, uncovered and untreated, were used to form the roof construction, a move that, although driven by financial limitations, has provided the living space with an increase in volume and better proportions that if a conventional ceiling had been installed. None of this can be seen from the street: it is only from the rear yard that the house can be understood as having been almost entirely replaced, its plain masonry walls at ground level providing a firm base for the upper floor's timber superstructure and protective shell of steel cladding that gives some clue to the combination of pragmatism and architectural ingenuity that has transformed a relatively anonymous early 20th century dwelling into a unique home suited to 21st century family life.

**Atherden Road,
Lower Clapton, London** (2010)
Hugh Strange Architects
Photographer: David Grandorge

Chapter 8
The Extended Timber House

Long considered the humblest of architectural endeavours, the house extension as a building type has nevertheless often provided the test bed for new ideas about the arrangement and use of domestic space, irrespective of property size or cost of construction. Yes, the term 'home extension' is invariably considered to be synonymous with the words 'small' and 'cheap', but the modern house addition can often be quite large, even to the point of exceeding the size of the building it connects to. The house extension may well also not be cheap: depending upon brief, location, required quality, size and ease of response to external factors such as local planning and site conditions, as well as the level of construction costs prevailing in the immediate area, the final price can sometimes approach eye-watering levels of expense.

The simplest and potentially least-costly opportunity for extension is usually to the side or rear of an existing house where design is primarily constrained by the amount of land area available and by local planning authority determination as to the extent of new building works allowable in terms of plot size, height, proximity to adjacent properties and choice of materials. The challenge becomes more complex if the home to be extended is Listed or if the property sits within a Conservation Area, each of which brings the relationship of the new to the old into the discussion and the degree to which the modern should complement or contrast with the past.

All this before any consideration of engineering or constructional issues, such as existing ground conditions and their effect upon foundation options; site accessibility for large-size components and whether there is available storage space for materials; and the choice to build onsite using traditional methods or to employ modern, offsite manufacturing technologies to prefabricate easily assembled elements. And then there is cost, the critical factor that determines the final decision on so many of these choices. The answers to these and many other questions are interdependent and ensuring that the majority aid and abet each other towards a holistic design solution is the difference between the creation of an architecturally coherent response to the existing building or of a confection of ill-considered forms, spaces and materials. This, in a nutshell, is why the humble house extension is often not quite so humble: each design response to brief, budget and physical and technological constraints is individual and, when well done, can deliver a unique—and often economically beneficial (in terms of energy use as well as property values)—addition to the host building.

The decision to extend is almost always primarily due to the desire for more space. Of course, the economics involved have an influential role to play, in that it may be less expensive to add floor area than to move to a larger property, but it may also be that it is not convenient to relocate away from an existing workplace, local health facilities, schools, etc.: constraints that necessitate some rethinking and/or redesign of room layouts and available garden space or other outside area.

**147 De Beauvoir Road,
Kingsland,
London Borough of Hackney**
(2013)
Scott Architects
Photography: Lyndon Douglas

**51A Gloucester Crescent,
London Borough of Camden**
(2010)

John Glew Architects
Photography: John Glew

The other characteristic—misconception, even—long associated with the design of house extensions is that it is predominantly the fiefdom of either the recently graduated designer who has been given a first opportunity to build by family or friends, or of the 70% or so of architectural practices in the UK that have fewer than ten employees and for whom a substantial part of their business's general workload is often founded on a diet of small projects. Whilst both of these categories may once have constituted the norm, increased property values in many parts of the UK have shifted opportunities for domestic extension several notches up the construction cost ladder and placed them within the sight-lines of larger, well-established architectural practices better known for their work on non-domestic building projects. At this cost level too, a sizeable number of architectural practices are to be found around the country that, whilst relatively small in terms of employee numbers, have consistently worked in the high quality (and high cost) end of the domestic market and who produce exquisitely designed and constructed projects for often-demanding clientele.

It is significant that at both economic extremes of the house extension market – and for whatever size of project – the use of timber has not only become more readily accepted over the past decade, but that many highly original wood-based solutions have emerged: timber construction systems, engineered products and advanced technologies previously assumed to be unaffordable in domestic projects are now being regularly employed to positive cost effect. There is little mystery as to the reason for this: timber in its simplest form is an ideal material for experimentation and innovation and, as architects and engineers have become more experienced with the range and availability of modern timber products, so too has their enthusiasm to explore the boundaries of each increased. Nowadays, the house extension is rightfully considered to be a legitimate building type in its own right, with the capacity to test ideas, materials and construction techniques before applying them to the larger challenges involved in the delivery of new housing in the UK.

Take for example, small sites at the end of existing terraces or where the space between buildings is not restricted by a right to light or by access or ventilation requirements—gap opportunities that our larger metropolitan areas still offer in reasonable abundance. The tiny, zinc-clad extension to the side elevation of a 1950s developer-built, two-storey cottage in the London Borough of Camden is just such a case: deceptive in its apparent simplicity, **51A Gloucester Crescent** (2010), by architect John Glew, sits on land never intended to be built upon, it being an extremely narrow, tapering space between the host dwelling—a small, plain brick box—and the flank wall of an adjacent semi-detached property, also two-storeys in height. Set back from the building line of the imposing Victorian brick and white stucco villas that form much of the Crescent, these three houses seem anachronistic, squeezed as they are between much taller, more urban buildings, with the slim 'bookend' in question considerably, yet very subtly, enhancing the uninspired architecture of the group.

The extension matches the host property in depth, the planes of its front and rear elevations kept parallel to the existing facades, thus avoiding any interruption of the garden areas in each instance. With so little plot area to work within, a conventional masonry extension would have narrowed the site even further, especially as exhaustive Party Wall negotiations had, in the end, necessitated the construction of a separate gable wall, independent of the neighbouring property. The insulated timber frame solution arrived at has not only minimised the depth of this end plane but has also allowed an extremely narrow passage to be created between the front and back gardens. The space used to provide this access route has been recaptured at first floor level, the upper part of the house being jettied out to almost touch its neighbour. The frame itself has been set out with great precision, the stud positions echoed on the outer face of the walls where the seams of the zinc-clad panels stand a consistent 25mm proud of the surface and set at exactly the same centres as the timbers behind.

There is much more sophistication to be discovered in the design of the timber elements of this ultra-small annex: the front wall has a dual depth, the section of the frame closest to the existing building expanded to align with the brickwork, with the main part of the wall appearing to sit back from this to create, overall, an asymmetrical facade that reveals its relative thicknesses and thin-nesses in the oak linings of the window surrounds. For a necessarily small extension, the fastidious articulation of its details can only be admired. The imperatives of timber frame construction have predicated a multi-layered and highly intellectual architectural response that is belied by the project's deliberate understatement and its diminutive scale. The approach taken here to the use of timber—if applied in considerably larger buildings—could well set a new and higher bar to meet by others using this method of construction.

As with the Party Wall issues at 51A Gloucester Crescent, legal technicalities can either blight, and even prevent, a proposed addition to a building or they can inspire a far more unexpected, and infinitely more creative, solution. In the case of the **Austen House** (2015), by Adam Knibb Architects, the client undertook all the legal proceedings necessary to secure permission for a 'flying freehold' over the gap next to his home, the former toilet block of the old St. Swithun's School. The school had relocated in 1929, following which the main section of the former building became a library, with other parts sold off for residential use, including the—now renamed—Austen House. The gap in question was subject to a "right of passage", a legal burden that meant an access way had to be kept clear for the very rare occasions when a vehicle through route might be required. To further complicate matters, the old school is located along the North Walls road, a traffic route that runs within the Winchester town centre conservation area, with planning conditions attached that stipulated any addition should stand out from the existing building in both design and materials.

Needing more space, the clients' brief also included their wish for a south-facing aspect and more natural light which, together with the legal, physical and planning constraints of the site, resulted in the design of a cantilevered 'pod' that extends out of the first floor of the house and, as with 51A Gloucester Crescent, stopping fractionally short of the neighbouring building. Two slender metal posts support the extreme edge of the cantilever but, in conformity with the requirement that the extension should visibly distinguish itself from the main house and the adjoining buildings, only the seemingly levitating pod can be seen from the road, the view to its undercroft screened behind tall, solid timber gates. Partly prefabricated offsite to speed onsite assembly and minimise disruption, the pod is clad with full length (i.e. no joins), western red cedar boards installed vertically to contrast with the horizontality of the brickwork of the existing buildings and to draw the eye up over the gate and through the aligned front and rear windows to the sky beyond. Other full height vertical windows to front and rear demarcate the timber cladding from the brickwork of the Austen House, further emphasising the pod's accomplishment in meeting the requirement to distinguish itself architecturally from its neighbours.

In setting the front elevation of the pod slightly back from the facade of the main house, the extension sits marginally forward of the rear corner of the adjacent building, allowing the windows in the length of its west elevation to have views over the garden wall. This, plus the creation of a south elevation with its Juliet balcony and a sky lantern over the room have combined to deliver the clients' desire for a south-facing aspect and maximum daylight. A complex package of requirements resolved as a simple, inexpensive timber box (£45k), albeit a remarkably unconventional one.

**Austen House,
North Walls, Winchester** (2015)
Adam Knibb Architects
Photography: Martin Gardner

These last two adjectives might equally be applied to the **Dairy House** (2008) on the 850 acre (345 hectare) Hadspen Estate at Castle Cary in Somerset by architects Skene Catling de la Peña, but perhaps with even greater emphasis since, in this case, the design of the extension to the existing building is amongst the most imaginative in conception and original in its timber construction as can be found anywhere in the country. The project began with a conventional set of requirements: the removal of a number of lean-to sheds and the re-planning of—and addition to—a former dairy building that had previously been converted to cottage use in order to create five bedrooms, three bathrooms (two of which are in the extension), better-proportioned rooms and more generous circulation space. The brief also called for the reformed dairy to combine privacy and seclusion with openness to the wider landscape; to appear unchanged from the outside; and for the new-build extension to appear as a natural part of the existing structure.

With these criteria to the fore, the architects set out to make the extension, appear 'undesigned', with the required sense of retreat reinforced through 'camouflage', i.e. with its form and massing echoing and complementing that of the existing structure. The flank elevation of the main dwelling is paralleled by a retaining wall, at the storey-height of each of which is fixed a large steel beam. The gable ends of the extension are designed to function as rigid beams that span between these planes, passing over the wall before returning inwards at right angles to frame one end of an outdoor bathing pool, the water of which is held back by the tanked structure.

A key construction aim was to use as many local materials as possible, particularly estate timber which was planked and dried in the storage barns in the farmyard opposite the site. The traditional drying method employed—stacked raw planks separated by spacers to facilitate air circulation—became the generator of both the logic and the aesthetic of the extension, whereby stout, waney-edge English oak planks have been stacked in the manner of traditional log cabins, the gaps between each being filled with thick slabs of laminated glass. The layers increase in depth towards the base to reinforce the sense of weight and rustication. Where the timbers meet at right angles and sit board-on-board, a re-entrant corner has been cut in

The Dairy House, Somerset
(2008)
Skene Catling de la Pena
Photography: James Morris

each to define a stratified vertical post—an ingenious detail that not only elegantly resolves the conundrum of how to articulate the building's primary junctions, but which also contrasts the rustic outer edges of the planks with the quality of fine joinery to be found in furniture-making. Indeed, the timber structure was assembled on site using prefabricated elements cut and finished in the workshop of local cabinet maker, Paul Longpré, less than two miles from the site.

The laminated glass layers were also produced by a specialist glass worker based nearby, each long slab sitting on a rubber gasket which, in turn, sits on the timber. Foam seals sit on the surface of the blocks to form weatherproof movement joints, with clear silicon forming the final seal, a technique never previously used in glass construction. Inside, the glass is polished and the timber finely sanded. The overall effect of this layering of the oak and the laminated float glass is to produce an ethereal, filtered quality to the changes in natural light changes through the day, dematerialising the building through reflection and refraction. At night, the addition becomes a glowing lantern, a lighthouse in its own aquatic landscape that delivers an almost magical experience and transcending standard interpretations of the term 'house extension'.

The Dairy House is not alone in being transformed for habitation: the English countryside in particular has seen many of its traditional timber-framed barns converted to dwellings with some also being extended, with varying degrees of success, to provide additional accommodation. Not all agricultural buildings whose original purpose has long gone were built with timber as their

**The Hurdle House,
Alresford, Hampshire** (2016)
Adam Knibb Architects
Photography: James Morris

The Hurdle House, Alresford, Hampshire (2016)
Adam Knibb Architects
Photography: James Morris

predominant structural material: other forms of construction are more usually considered to best represent the country's built heritage and to thus merit Listed Building status. One such is the **Hurdle House** (2016), by Adam Knibb Architects, on the edge of Alresford, a small Hampshire town that, by the end of the 18th century had become the location for one of the four largest sheep fairs in the country. The (then) barn was constructed in 1835 to store the wooden hurdles used to form the sheep pens used at these events and justifies its Grade II status not only as a relic of the area 's industrial archaeology but by virtue of its elegantly proportioned wall construction, a combination of knapped flints edged with rubbed red brick quoins and punctuated with string courses of the same material. The pitched roof above the single-storey masonry structure is covered with red clay tiles that have weathered to a darker, harmonious tone. The building is oriented north-south, facing east onto a gravelled forecourt and with a large garden to the north.

In the not-too-distant past, planning conditions in such circumstances would often have looked for slavish replication of materials and details in any new addition. Times change, however, with, in this instance, Winchester City Council's Conservation Department taking a rather more enlightened view of the proposal to construct the extension from wood. In part, this latitude can be attributed to a preference for the project to have a distinctively modern appearance to contrast with the existing, but also for the material's relationship to the expansive landscape surrounding the property. The Department agreed that the bay window in the barn's north gable could be removed to provide the opening for a linking element between it and the addition an opportunity that has resulting in a frameless glass box that lightly touches the existing building and facilitates the transition in levels between the old and the new.

The 'new' is an uncompromisingly modern, but simple, oak-clad box, the thin metal coping to which aligns neatly with the top-most brick string course of the existing building, giving the impression that a continuous line connects the two. The long, low addition also provides physical separation between the forecourt and the garden, whilst permitting views through to the latter. In other circumstances perhaps, the box-like structure could be formed as a frame, but here the extension is given strength and solidity through the use of cross laminated timber. Until relatively recently this would have been considered uneconomic for a one-off, single-storey building, but other considerations are increasingly balancing conventional value engineering approaches with more sophisticated analysis of the long term benefits of prefabricated solid panels such as reduced onsite workmanship, resulting in efficient, speedy construction; and minimum material wastage (other benefits can be found in Chapter 3, the Solid Timber

House). In this instance, the delivery and assembly of the panels took a mere five days and, with confidence in the accuracy of their fabrication, the glazing package had been pre-ordered from computer drawings and fitted the following week. It is a design and construction strategy fast coming of age for new build housing in the UK.

Access issues and a minimal budget precluded the use of CLT for the long, low timber extension to a Grade-B listed Georgian terrace house in Edinburgh's **Bonnington Grove** (2015), by Konishi Gaffney Architects. Here the 36 metre long and relatively narrow 9 metre wide garden was not only urban, but provided unusual challenges. First amongst these was the non-statutory planning guidance that stated listed buildings in the city should have no more than 50% of their rear elevation built across, a problem in this case due to the fact that an existing, late-Victorian addition already occupied the west half of the facade. Agreement that the addition would not connect to the main house across the other half of the elevation threw up another hurdle: the extension would have to be sunk down into the ground to ensure that the resultant courtyard could not easily be glazed over to form an illicit conservatory, a requirement with inevitable, harmful, budget consequences.

In response, the architects' chose to locate the addition against the garden wall that shadowed the site from the east and away from the house's rear elevation but umbilically connected to it via the existing extension. Cost considerations also led them to revisit the construction method developed in the 1960s by architect Walter Segal, a rigorous, but simple timber framing system that was gratefully adopted by self-builders then for its ease and economy and which now, with increasingly unaffordable property prices and pronounced housing shortages, is undergoing something of a renaissance. Thus, a concrete and blockwork base was sunk one metre into

Bonnington Grove, Edinburgh (2015)
Konishi Gaffney Architects
Photography: Andrew Lee

the garden and tanked up to damp proof course level to form the plinth for a stick-built timber frame carefully set out at 600mm centres and expressed internally at the windows and in the joists below the ceiling of rough-sawn sarking boards. This being a kitchen, the boards have a coating of intumescent paint, whilst the walls and roof have 250mm of PUR insulation to compensate for the extent of glass relative to the extension's floor area.

Clever detailing of a trickle vent into the cladding cavity made the use of fixed windows possible and a benefit to the budget. All of the external timber has been painted, with the external plywood cladding fixed at the same centres as the glazing and detailed, in accordance with the principles of the Segal method, with cover strips to protect the joints. The expressed structure is accentuated by the building's low-slung proportions and extended eaves which, together with its covered outdoor seating area, was achieved at the astonishingly low cost of £52,000. Simple and affordable—and with more than a passing nod to the egalitarian genius of Walter Segal—the determined level of architectural intention that has underpinned the conception and delivery of this extension ably demonstrates that, when it comes to timber construction, clients should not presume that a restricted budget need result in a 'cheap' or low quality building. It would be entirely wrong to describe this project as a 'humble' extension: Bonnington Grove is a model solution to a multiplicity of regulatory and technical challenges.

In the world of additions proposed to existing buildings, tricky planning processes are not confined to those that carry 'Listed' status, especially when other regulatory issues also come into play. In the case of the extension to an Edwardian terrace house in East London's **Stamford Road** (2016) by Pamphilon Architects, height restrictions to one side of the narrow rear garden, as well as budget constraints, conflicted with the need to achieve as much headroom as possible to allow passage from the existing living room doorway. The neighbouring property on the other side had some large and very visible roof vents which, if the roof could be pushed up, would serve to conceal the offending items whilst still allowing clear ventilation.

The reason for confronting these difficulties lay in a badly built and wholly unattractive 1960s kitchen addition that was so narrow it could not actually accommodate a dining table. Fortunately, the kind of width restriction encountered at Bonnington Road do not always apply to terraced properties in London, albeit that there are often other technical challenges

Bonnington Grove, Edinburgh (2015)
Konishi Gaffney Architects
Photography: Andrew Lee

**Stamford Road,
Dalston,
London Borough of Hackney**
(2016)

Pamphilon Architects

Photographer: Anna Pamphilon

to address. The solution here involved the demolition of the previous structure and the construction of a new roof designed to extend over what had been a passageway from a door in the rear wall of the house to the garden. The limited funds available meant only one steel beam could be afforded, a design limitation turned to good effect in it being used to span the full length of the extension's asymmetrical roof and creating a completely clear floor area below. The beam acts as the spine to two sloping softwood-framed planes, the joists over the former passage exposed to view whilst, by way of contrast the other is boarded and plastered with two Velux windows introduced to illuminate the galley kitchen.

It is the garden elevation that is the extension's most distinctive feature, however: taking its design cue from the main house's 'butterfly' roof, the profile of the addition's Siberian larch cladding appears to echo its inverted angles whilst screening the variable pitches of the roof behind. Considerable attention has been given to the detailing of the cladding, with three different widths of boards employed. The plane of the rainscreen continues over an area that has been recessed to fulfil two functions: access to a manhole that could not be moved for cost reasons; and to signify the doorway between extension and garden. The distinction is emphasised in the cladding panel, where every other board has been omitted: a simple but effective device permitting more light to penetrate into the dining area. This attention to detail is extended to the simple bench outside the kitchen window—cantilevered out from the structure's brick plinth, its horizontal timber slats are spaced to align precisely with the vertical cladding boards above.

As with the extension at Bonnington Grove, the response here to tight budget constraints and site complexities is a simple, but highly effective solution to a client's need for more space. What distinguishes it from the mass of modern house extensions, however, is the way in which its architect has used this small project to explore the creative possibilities inherent in the timber cladding of its exterior and, in doing so, to produce a quite out-of-the-ordinary result.

Rear extensions are not, of course, always low budget nor indeed do they need to take a rectilinear form, as is evidenced by the curvaceous forms of the addition to **147 De Beauvoir Road** (2013), by Scott Architects. Situated in a conservation area in the London Borough of Hackney, the long garden to the three-bedroom Victorian terrace house has been used to the full in providing not only a spacious, semi-sunken kitchen and dining area, but also an unusual

timber-clad curved room at first floor level. The form of the extension was largely determined by limits imposed by the local authority on the addition's overall height and depth as well as the need to ensure adequate daylight to neighbouring windows. Nothing of this is at all evident from the formality of the street elevation but, behind the extensively remodelled house is a hidden world of overlapping curved walls, floors and inclined surfaces intended, in the words of the architect, "to express the interiors as a series of fluid surfaces and flowing spaces that dip, soar and weave through the house, leading to west-facing outdoor spaces that gently extend over the dining room as a green roof of sedum, grass and wild flowers."

Achieving all of this was hardly a simple operation: with access to the site limited, a prefabricated steel frame had to be brought through the house and assembled on a concrete floor slab, with the sloping green roof above supported on a plywood deck. The garden itself has been divided into a series of zones that, at its lowest level, seamlessly connects an outdoor cooking area with the interior kitchen/dining space, the two separated only by a bespoke folding screen. More than this, however, it is the extensive use of vertical oak cladding, both inside and out, that gives the addition's organic forms their homogeneous quality: combining both solid and punctured screen walls, the vertical timber curves and flows on plan, with the sinuous external wall of the first floor room above echoed in outline in the timber panel that is planted onto the dining area's plastered ceiling. A hybrid structure this may be, but it is its sculpted form, as if carved out of the garden landscape, together with the careful modulation of the quality, natural materials employed throughout, that provides the De Beauvoir Road extension with the sense of it having almost preceded the house it has been designed to adjoin. This is skilful architecture, in which the warmth and richness of the oak cladding has been used in beautiful complement to the other materials used.

Throughout the world, urban environments continue to be densified in response to changing demographics and the final variation of the house extension to be explored here is that in which the building is expanded upwards. A lack of developable vacant sites combined with a

147 De Beauvoir Road,
Kingsland,
London Borough of Hackney
(2013)
Scott Architects
Photography: Lyndon Douglas

growing predilection to retain existing structures rather than to demolish and replace them with new housing or apartment blocks has stimulated interest in the possibility of topping buildings with one or more additional storeys. The benefits of doing so are many, including: the ability to increase the overall floor area and height of a structure without significantly increasing the load on the existing foundations; the extension of existing service connections rather than confront the cost and timescale implications associated with the installation of new electric, gas and water facilities; the replacement of old roofs and underused and uninsulated roofspace with new, thermally efficient enclosures to cap the older structures; and the potential to prefabricate lightweight elements that can be quickly craned into position and complete projects speedily, thus obviating the need to identify and establish new building sites with all their attendant traffic and storage problems. In the delivery of this new dimension of urban architecture, the use of timber construction products and systems scores highly, being lighter in weight than most alternative technologies and arguably more adaptable to bespoke offsite prefabrication.

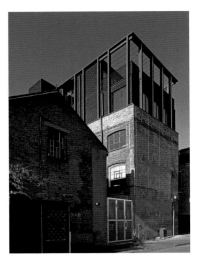

An excellent example of how to do this well can be found at the **Black House** (2017) in the London Fields area of Hackney. Designed by Simon Conder Architects, a practice widely recognised for its many outstanding timber-based projects, the addition is a 255 sq/m home for clients who own and work out of the three-storey, brick-built Victorian warehouse below. In order to contain the budget and to avoid disruption to both their design business and to neighbouring properties, a two-storey, prefabricated timber extension was devised, the lower floor of which contains two bedrooms, two bathrooms, a utility room and a studio. The building's circulation core continues from here to the next level, arriving into a large, open-plan living area on its west side, with a kitchen/dining area to its east, and an external decked loggia structure beyond. The structural frame and lift shaft have been formed from glulam beams and columns made of European larch, with thin, super-insulated timber cassette panels providing the external walls, roof and internal floors, reflecting the limited loadings that could be supported on the host building's existing foundations. All of these elements were prefabricated by an offsite manufacturer in South Yorkshire before being delivered to site for installation.

The grid of the warehouse's windows has been followed in the setting out of the externally expressed glulam columns in order to form a visual link between the old and the new. Horizontal weatherboarding installed between the columns protects the high thermal performance cassette panels, with wall openings on the north elevation minimised to further reduce heat loss. A larger number of window openings appear on the east and south facades to maximise sunlight and passive solar gain, with protruding external shades introduced at top floor level to reduce overheating. All of the external timber elements, including the slender lift shaft that provides direct access from the ground floor to the apartment above, have been finished in a matt black preservative stain that contrasts well with the warehouse's yellow, London stock brick, wall structure.

Unlike all of the other extensions featured in this chapter which have been shown to provide accommodation to existing houses in which timber in various forms has been a fundamental part of the design, that to the Black House has delivered a completely independent and totally timber-based house on top of a warehouse that continues to be used for industrial purposes. As such, this robust, well-proportioned and crisply detailed timber home has been designed to respect the industrial character of the original building whilst modestly emphasising its own contemporary architectural credentials. It is a sterling example of how the urgent demand for new inner city housing might be met in the post-industrial metropolitan areas of the UK, and in doing so introduce a healthier, more humane and sustainable form of architecture founded upon intelligent use of timber in all its many forms.

**Black House,
Fortescue Avenue,
Hackney, London** (2017)
Simon Conder Architects
Photography: Paul Smoothy

Chapter 9
The Suburban Timber House

Suburbia—the swathes of housing developed on the edge of many of Britain's metropolitan areas—is so much a part of life today for a large percentage of the UK's population that it seems to have always been with us. However, the term only dates back some 120 years and evolved with particular reference to London. Camberwell in south-east London (and just under three miles from Charing Cross), for example, was, until 1889, part of the County of Surrey and although the original parish became the Metropolitan Borough of Camberwell in 1900, it was still considered to be suburban until well into the 1920s. The same is true for many other parts of the capital such as Highgate and Wandsworth, once distinctive villages in their own right, which are now fully absorbed into the fabric of the UK's largest city.

Suburbs were once seen as places to escape to: an alternative location in which life could be enjoyed away from the violence, vice and disease synonymous with the 19th century metropolis. As our cities have expanded, however, the cost of residing in them has increased exponentially, forcing many to live further and further away from their place of employment: there is now an abundance of large-scale extensions to suburbs which have become townships in their own right. Meanwhile, areas previously considered to be suburbs have been densified: large, single-use family villas have been subdivided into apartments and workspaces, their leafy gardens shortened to permit additional residential development in the grounds, whilst others have simply been demolished to enable new, taller blocks of housing to be constructed. The pressures on the coherence of traditional, leafy suburban streets are immense: the inherent design challenge is how the growing intensification of suburban built fabric might emulate, rather than imitate, what has gone before: we are no longer creating streets of identical detached villas, semi-detached houses or bungalows in the suburban landscape, but infilling gaps that have emerged in the rows of pattern-book units or finding opportunity on land previously regarded as their private Arcadia by individual home owners.

Successful solutions to the often complex planning issues involved are rarely to be found in the standardised house types offered by builder-developers and considerations of sustainability also have their part to play in this ongoing re-evaluation of the suburban tradition: should the materials employed simply replicate those of existing buildings or can complementary ones with improved environmental credentials be used? Can new interventions in the suburban landscape embrace passive design principles and be receptive to the introduction of renewable energy technology? Can their construction take advantage of modern offsite fabrication processes and thereby reduce the building timescale, avoid unnecessary wastage of materials and minimise disturbance to neighbours? These same criteria can be found in other chapters of this book, but ideas on how they might be applied in new suburban projects, that are often predicated on design responses arising from the physical and planning constraints of an unusual site are where opportunities to introduce greater—and more creative—use of timber have been progressively emerging.

Herringbone Houses,
Lyford Road,
Wandsworth, London (2007)
Alison Brooks Architects
Photographer: Christobal Palma

149

The earliest example included here of timber usage in modern suburban housing is to be found to the south west of Wandsworth Common in London. Lyford Road is lined with alternating detached and semi-detached, two-storey, room-in-roof, red brick Edwardian homes of a style common to many prosperous London suburbs. Two separate bowling club buildings break the rhythm of the street, with land once owned by one of them providing a flat site for the **Herringbone Houses** (2007), a two-house development designed by Alison Brooks Architects. The houses are approached on the bowling green side via a 45 metre-long driveway and are thus set well back from the street, with their front elevations facing onto the green itself. Apart from a handful of minor design variations, they initially seem identical in form: each is comprised of a main, three-storey volume with a two-storey side wing arranged perpendicular to the street in AB-AB formation, rather than a mirrored AB-BA which, because of their close proximity to each other, appears (unless looked at frontally) as a conjoined series of alternating cuboidal blocks that conceals the detached nature of the two houses.

It is the striking appearance of the front and rear facades that distinguishes these houses. No attempt has been made to replicate the stuccoed bay windows and gables or the hipped roofs that form the character of the area; the Herringbone Houses instead convey their uncompromising modernity through the radical design of their external timber cladding. Formed from Ipe (sometimes referred to as Brazilian Walnut), one of the hardest and most durable of tropical hardwood species whose density makes it extremely difficult to work, the material was pre-cut into 800mm lengths and fixed at an angle of 22.5 degrees in alternate horizontal bands to provide the houses with their distinctive herringbone pattern. The optical effect of this is given a further, three-dimensional twist in the chamfering of the reveals to the principal windows on the first and second floors. In a design as innovative as this, detail is unquestionably the key to success and, in this instance, a single hole was pre-drilled at either end of each board to house the countersunk stainless steel screws that fix the cladding to softwood battens. These are themselves fixed to vertical battens to provide a continuous ventilation gap behind the exterior timber. The craftsmanlike precision given to this fixing method is exemplified by the laborious sanding-off that was carried out on the Ipe plugs impressed into each screw hole.

Internally, the stair to each house has been set to one side of a top-lit, two-storey central hallway, allowing a direct view from the front door through to the rear garden. The staircase

**Herringbone Houses,
Lyford Road,
Wandsworth, London** (2007)
Alison Brooks Architects
Photographer: Christobal Palma

**Chestnut,
Newport Road,
Barnes, West London** (2010)
David Long Architects
Photographer: David Long

from ground to first floor appears as a dark stained, solid oak object, the stairs and risers of which provide a serrated edge that is matched by the undercroft of the stair from the first to the second floor, an illusory device intended to suggest both elements have been fractured apart from a very large solid block of wood.

Overall, The Herringbone Houses' highly contemporary application of timber can be seen to be firmly grounded in the tradition of English timber-framed houses in which square, structural infill panels are given diagonal patterns for bracing and decorative purposes. Similarly, the delineation of the Ipe cladding in horizontal bands as a proportioning device has its precedent in Renaissance stonework.

A 25 minute drive north-west to another leafy London suburb—this time in Barnes—Newport Road is rather less coherent from an architectural perspective, but, perhaps as an indication of the ubiquity of the red brick and stucco house-type, **Chestnut** (2010) by David Long Architects stands immediately adjacent to a semi-detached property of similar pattern-book vintage and style to those found in Wandsworth's Lyford Road. Built on a plot formerly occupied by garages, the two-storey house's external appearance of two separate blocks linked by a glazed core suggests it is much larger than it actually is, an impression given additional emphasis by the fact that the building fabric extends to the boundary walls on each of its four sides.

Intriguingly, entrance to the house is not directly through the high street wall, but via a timber door into a small courtyard, the first of four small external areas that form the voids between the building and the site's perimeter. Directly ahead lies the sitting room, with a view through its sliding glass walls to another external terrace, but the sequence of reaching it requires a right turn through the front door into a small hallway. The outside parking area can be seen immediately ahead; to the right is a cloakroom; the living room lies to the left, as does the first sight of the oak and glass staircase that connects the five interlocking half-levels of this two-storey (plus basement) home. Unusually, the stair flights are set perpendicular to the glazed

core within which they rise, a subtle design move that, in providing direct access to each floor, has eschewed the need for additional landings and allowed an open plan arrangement to be effected throughout all the public areas of the house.

Set on a reinforced concrete basement, the house's large-section timber frame is expressed externally at both ground and rear half basement levels, with timber-framed glazed sliding doors set behind the line of the structure. This, together with the direct relationship between lower floor levels and external courtyards, not only enables maximum natural light to reach into these floors, but also has the effect of raising into the air those parts of the house that appear to be more solid: a structural solution synonymous with the tenets of modernist architecture, but fabricated in wood rather than concrete. Above this, the upper floors are faced with untreated sweet chestnut cladding that has been sourced in the south-east of England. Matching folding shutters are set within the horizontally-laid cladding and can be partially closed to provide solar shading or flush to ensure privacy and security.

The theme of a central, top-lit, triple-height hall—a characteristic of many larger, traditional suburban properties—also appears in a visually more radical house in the southern suburbs of Cambridge. Cavendish Avenue is a tree-lined enclave of large Victorian homes of what might be termed diverse architectural character. Designed by Mole Architects and almost contemporary with the Herringbone Houses, this striking property replaced a detached house built in the 1930s that was deemed to be uncomfortably small and comprised of a series of unfriendly spaces. That it also manifested a clumsy combination of architectural styles rendered it beyond adaptation and reuse and the owners sought out Mole Architects to provide them with a contemporary villa that would make a positive contribution to the overall architectural quality of the street. The new house was thus conceived to be an exemplar in its design, scale and construction: ambitions that, perhaps inevitably, attracted some resistance during the planning application process. In the end, the vote in committee was split 4:4, but the chair's casting vote fell in the project's favour because of the proposal's outstanding green qualities, credentials that have since been more than proven in the actuality: to all intents and purposes, the building achieves the AECB Passivhaus benchmark for overall energy use.

**Cavendish Avenue,
Cambridge** (2008)
Mole Architects
Photographer: David Butler

In plan the main form of the house at **Cavendish Avenue** (2008) is simple enough: essentially tripartite, it has a conventional grid arrangement that embraces the top-lit main hall and staircase that binds the building's three levels and its many rooms into the relatively conventional arrangement of public rooms at ground floor and bedrooms on the two floors above. Attached to the front is the first of the house's more unusual features: a square room with an asymmetrical, pyramidic roof clad completely with cedar shingles. This engaged pavilion, with its corner window, stands almost as a guard house to the main entrance and as a stark, textured material contrast to the flat plate of fritted glass that forms the principal elevation. Here, the house is at its most classical in conception: an abstraction of base, middle and top that provides an outward view from the top, attic storey landing but, at *piano nobile* level, reveals only the rising staircase instead of the anticipated principal room.

Once inside, the house's timber structure reveals itself: the oak of the staircase and walkways to the first and second floors contrasting with the exposed glulam columns and beams that support the cross laminated timber floor plates, the soffits of which have been given a translucent white Osma stain. The main walls are also of 117mm thick cross laminated timber, lined on the inside and highly insulated on the exterior with an over-cladding of cement fibre rainscreen panels. Aside from the elegance of the main staircase, the pièce de résistance from a timber construction perspective is, however, the interior of the shingle-clad pavilion, where KLH's cross laminated timber structure has been completely exposed to view, conveying both warmth and acoustic benefit to a room primarily used for playing, and listening to, music.

In contrast to the front facade, the south (garden) elevation appears as a two-storey, rendered wall through which the horizontal glulam beams have been projected to connect with further horizontal and vertical glulam elements to creating a double-height, tetrastyle loggia structure that, in summer, acts as a frame for adjustable external fabric sunshades.

Any controversy over the design of this house in Cavendish Avenue is long over: the Planning Department at Cambridge City Council apparently now holds the building up as an example of how to do a 'modern' traditional house: truly, a contemporary timber classic.

Further north, the small town of Worsley lies within the metropolitan area of Salford and, being some 5.75 miles west of Manchester itself, within easy commuting distance of the northern metropolis. The completion in 1761 of the Bridgewater Canal allowed Worsley to expand from a small village of cottage industries to an important base for cotton manufacture, iron-working, brick-making and extensive coal mining. The town expanded further after WWI and WWII with the addition of new housing estates. One such is the location for **Woodstock** (2008) by the Stephenson Studio. In its original form, the house was bought by its owner purely for its proximity to the centre of Worsley, but its standardised house-type layout was neither efficient nor made best use of its site in a gently sloping suburban street. Consequently, the decision was made to remodel the entire dwelling to provide accommodation that would be more flexible and responsive to modern family life.

The subsequent transformation of the existing, very unremarkable, house has been nothing short of dramatic: whilst maintaining the building line of the street elevation and the principal angle of the asymmetrical roofs on adjacent dwellings, the external appearance of the house no longer bears even passing resemblance to its neighbours. The most fundamental and obvious change made has been in the materials used: the brown brick and PVC windows of its predecessor and of the adjoining properties has been replaced on the upper levels of the house with timber cladding that is neatly fixed in horizontal bands of alternating width and which step down to meet the front door in recognition of the split level that exists internally on either side of the entrance. The striation of the cladding extends around the side elevation and, again, to the rear facade where it wraps around the large sliding doors that separate the upper living area from an external terrace. This terrace forms the roof to the house-wide, ground level deck that mediates between the very modern open-plan kitchen/dining area and the garden.

The timber carapace constructed to surround the house also provides a strong visual indicator of the Tardis-like metamorphosis that has taken place in its interior. Given the unprepossessing nature of the street and of Woodstock's forebear, this house now stands as an exemplar for what might be done to upgrade the tens of thousands of existing suburban homes whose configuration is unsuited to the many and ongoing changes in the ways that modern families live their lives. It is clear why the Manchester Society of Architects judged it the winner of the Small Scale Residential category in its 2009 Awards.

Built only a few years later, the overall floor area of the double house project at **25-25a Hurst Avenue** (2013) in London's Highgate by Waugh Thistleton Architects is almost exactly the same as that of the Herringbone Houses (being 2 x 400sq/m) but the design solution could not be more different. The site in this case slopes steeply, providing the opportunity for open-plan, split-level floor plates and sunken terraces and long uninterrupted views through the entire length of the house. Set back from the street, the front elevation appears as a mirrored, two-storey structure, the main entrance doors set next to the spine wall that separates the two properties. The ground floor of each house has an en-suite bedroom, kitchen and family living space, whilst the level above contains a 100sq/m double aspect reception room that links the front of the house to the rear garden. Above, set back and less visible from the street is a master bedroom and two further en-suite bedrooms. A separate studio sits to the rear of the garden as part of the overall development.

Structurally, the Hurst Avenue properties represent a relatively early use of cross laminated timber (by KLH UK) in a housing development that, whilst aimed at the luxury end of the market, would not previously have been considered to be large enough to suggest an economic use of this engineered timber product. The benefits of doing so (good thermal properties and high levels of airtightness) would appear to have met the developers' criteria to create efficient, low energy buildings. That the erection of the project's main superstructure could be completed in just six days by only six men was also a compelling reason for its selection.

Added to this has been the use of Kebony® to clad both houses, the Hurst Avenue properties being the first UK residential project to feature this environmentally-friendly material. Kebony® (see chapter 4 for more details) has a minimal carbon footprint, with just 10% of the CO_2 emissions created in the production of clear-fell Brazilian Ipe, its specification perhaps indicative of the degree of change in the sustainability concerns of metropolitan developers in the six intervening years between the construction of the Herringbone Houses in Wandsworth and these properties. Indeed, the developers have carried its use through the extensive outdoors decking and exterior furnishings including the post box, refuse bin stores and the garden gates. These houses are without doubt at the top end of the market, but the extensive use of timber in their structure and cladding make clear that the many advantages inherent in the use of engineered and modified wood products are now having a significant impact on all sectors of development and construction.

It should be said that the two homes at Hurst Avenue—and indeed the dual Herringbone Houses before them—present bespoke architectural responses to the specific site conditions their architects and clients have encountered. For a variety of reasons including size, cost and planning restraints, solutions of this sort are not necessarily easily transferable to the more usual design challenges that continue to emerge in the UK's suburban areas.

One such is the smaller semi-detached house: one of the most recognisable features of the suburban world, it is efficient in land use, internal planning and in construction materials. Variations of the type exist in every part of the UK and in both private and public sector housing, yet its renewal or reinterpretation provides a significant design problem: the densification of available suburban land has bred a plethora of house types from many different housing developers that, tightly packed onto the available land, allow only the minimum required separating distance between adjacent dwellings. This uncomfortable proximity has often been more about creating a distinctive market identity for the house as a brand than any ability to contribute in a meaningful way to successful place-making. Weak attempts to provide some notional, traditional architectural character to the semi-detached model have also resulted in many incoherent developments that, in both layout and streetscape, show little of the positive qualities that give places their character and which render them attractive to residents. Whilst there has been numerous attempts over the years to develop new suburban house forms, these have often focused on the design of individual units and not on their capacity for harmonious repetition.

25-25a Hurst Avenue, Highgate, London (2013)
Waugh Thistleton Architects
Photographer: Bliss Space

This cannot be said of the **Cedar Lodges** (2015) in Winchester by Adam Knibb Architects, a pair of semi-detached homes whose contemporary design immediately distinguishes them from less confident attempts to re-interpret suburban housing models. As ever on land previously used for other purposes (in this case, a garage) the site conditions determined much of the architectural response but, in doing so, have generated a prototypical solution that has considerable potential for adaptation and replication elsewhere.

The site rises from the pavement edge to the back of the plot, a factor that prompted the decision to raise the homes above private garages that front almost directly onto the street and which are separated by projecting canopied entrances to each of the houses. This device has lifted normal suburban living rooms to their position as the building's principal spaces and set above the dark, monolithic 'basement' level. This classical ordering of space and form, emphasised by the single central mullion of the triangular windows that fill the roof gables, creates a pedimental effect and defines the otherwise un-fenestrated bedroom level as the building's attic storey. This simple arrangement has given the mirrored double frontage a sense of proportion, a factor further enhanced by the use of western red cedar cladding boards fixed vertically to what, in the conventional sequencing of levels, would be seen as the first and second floor street facade of the building.

The site is also long and thin, and the development draws upon local precedent in having narrow frontages from which the houses extend back in simple rectangular plan form to fill the entire depth of the plot. Outdoor spaces are incorporated at the sides rather than at the front or back and take the form of small gardens and decked areas accessed via sliding glazed units in the houses' respective kitchens. The bedrooms above have large picture windows out onto these spaces, augmented by skylight windows in the standing seam zinc roof and, in the rear elevation, by cedar-clad windows in housings skewed to ensure there is no direct view into the houses from adjoining properties.

Above their concrete and masonry podium, the Cedar Lodges are of prefabricated timber frame construction comprised of 175 x 47mm C24 studs at 400mm centres: a simple, accurate and economic system that confirms homes assembled in this way can not only be easily replicated but are also very well suited to self- and custom-build housing projects, particularly on awkward suburban sites that demand efficient, economic solutions. The Cedar Lodges' combination of elegant timber envelope and mirrored design simply begs to be replicated to produce extended streetscapes.

The examples above represent five very distinct approaches to what the nature and form of the future suburban house in the UK could be and how the fundamental characteristics of the typology might be repurposed to address critical issues arising from, for example, the country's changing demographics, the pressure of demand for housing in certain locations and the many differing ways that homes are nowadays used. Whether on flat or sloping sites and as detached, semi-detached or remodelled house types, the various timber species and products employed in the design and construction of these houses have had a discernible influence on their conception and ultimate appearance. Over a century on from the original definition of 'suburbia' (as highlighted at the beginning of this chapter), they also raise important questions, about the conception, layout, form and materials of future suburban developments. In the increasingly confused dimension of the built landscape that sits between the country's urban and rural environments, the case for using wood, in all its available manifestations, to define the UKs new suburbia, is compelling.

The Cedar Lodges,
Winchester, Hampshire (2015)
Adam Knibb Architects
Photographer: Martin Gardner

Chapter 10
The Regional Timber House

Discussion of regional distinctiveness in architecture is not new: it is almost 35 years since the internationally renowned architectural critic, Kenneth Frampton, published his seminal essay on Critical Regionalism, a term he posited as "the paradox: how to become modern and to return to sources; how to revive an old, dormant civilisation and take part in universal civilisation." This was an early identification of a phenomenon that is apparent in many parts of the world today: the desire to resist the homogeneity inherent in modern society and the construction industry's reflection of this in, as Frampton puts it, "the universal implementation of industrial techniques that work against the reflection of local culture in built-forms."

That was then and this is now: modern methods of construction and prefabrication have moved on considerably from the types of manufacturing processes that demanded constant production of identical elements in order to be efficient and cost effective. Offsite fabrication today offers considerable flexibility and creative possibilities as well as the potential to manufacture locally, an important factor in energy use considerations, as well as providing a catalyst for sustainable employment in remoter parts of the country.

A large number of the houses featured in this book are to be found in rural locations, designed to be site-specific in their response to local climate and landscape and to complement—or contrast with—the architectural traditions of the area. Often, particular conditions relating to form and materials are attached to the planning requirements for new buildings in rural situations; conditions that vary according to the cultural and environmental factors prevailing in different parts of the country and as formal replies to individual applications. The rural houses that appear throughout this book are highly individual in design and, often isolated in location, have established themselves as outstanding examples of a modern architectural genre that respects and engages positively with the UK's regional vernacular heritage whilst avoiding any lapse into a vernacular style.

Many of these dwellings are to be found in locations that might be regarded as relatively benign, weather-wise, and whilst situated in quite distinct areas of the country, have not been designed with the primary intention of providing modern typological models that can be translated into the design of multi-unit developments or communities. As such, it is difficult to imagine that, in time, they might—area-by-area—be considered to cumulatively represent new and authentic regional characters that, in response to changing demographics and rising land and property values are, ipso facto, the latest stage in the local cultural continuum.

There are however, parts of the UK, where something distinctive and part of the indigenous culture and landscape has been evolving. No area of the British Isles is better able to demonstrate regional distinctiveness in its modern architecture than the Isle of Skye where, over the past two decades or so, a swathe of new-build houses has emerged that, although individual in design, can nevertheless be seen collectively to more accurately reflect that which the Romans referred to as *genius loci*—the spirit of the place—than the crudely-designed and sited kit houses that have peppered the landscape for generations.

The history of the Isle of Skye—indeed of so many of the Inner and Outer Hebrides of Scotland—is a complex and often tragic collision of circumstances. First, there is its situation: close to the Scottish mainland, it nevertheless sits on the very edge of Europe, facing out to the Atlantic and, on a regular basis, in receipt of some of the wildest weather to hit the British Isles. Then there is the landscape: the rough, black igneous rock of the jagged-peaked Black Cuillin mountains and the granite of the adjoining Red Cuillin Hills effectively divides the north of the island from the south. Accessibility too, is a challenge: once over the Skye Bridge, there are relatively few roads leading off from the A87 that continues on to Uig on the west coast of the Trotternish peninsula. Three other factors have long dominated life in this unforgiving environment: the power and severity of the Church; land ownership (or the lack of); and the Gaelic language and culture.

Existence here for the native population was always hard: lacking land on which to grow food or nurture livestock, poverty and hunger were ever-present conditions. Clearances too (most recently in the 1920s when the Empire Settlement Act, an assisted passage programme, paid people to leave), took their toll on inhabitant numbers. To all intents and purposes, this was a dying community, lacking in hope and whose children were given a clear message at school: getting ahead is getting away. Depopulation is the curse of rural communities everywhere, but things in the Isle of Skye have gradually been changing and the historic decline is, to a certain extent, seeing some reverse today, with increasing numbers of people moving to Skye to avail themselves of the different pace and quality of life to be found there.

Housing, however, remains the island's biggest contemporary challenge: with the interest shown by relatively wealthy people from elsewhere in the possibility of living on Skye, existing properties have become expensive, as is land if one wishes to build anew. Neither is building an easy or straightforward task in an environment in which the confusing legalities of croft ownership still complicate where and what can be acquired. Construction costs too, are high: materials are generally brought from the mainland, the building season is short and the availability of skilled labour experienced in island conditions is variable. Seasonality also affects other things: a large part of the Skye economy nowadays is tourism-based, but employment in the industry is largely confined to the summer months and those involved who live permanently on the island invariably have at least one other job. Incomes for many are, as a consequence, low and insufficient to buy or

Tigh Port na Long, Aird of Sleat, Isle of Skye (2011)
Dualchas
Photographer: Andrew Lee

rent homes, even if enough suitable properties were available. The chronic lack of affordable homes is a significant problem that affects the lifeblood and future of Skye communities: two architectural practices, in particular, have chosen to address this, each with remarkable results.

Located at different ends of the island—Dualchas at Sleat in the south and Rural Design at Portree in the north—each has taken an unusual path, but, over the past two decades, both have concentrated the bulk of their endeavours on the design and construction of distinctively modern and energy-efficient houses that are rooted in indigenous models conditioned by Skye's environment and cultural traditions.

Formed in 1996, Dualchas chose from the outset to explore how the characteristics of the simple longhouse type, the Black House—"the single storey, turf and thatch, weather-resistant, wind-oriented shelter of custom and convenience that immemorially existed to house the agrarian Gael"—might be reinterpreted to meet contemporary building methods and standards and, in the synthesis of climate, design, materials and tradition, produce a new, indigenous form of architecture that could, on one hand, respond to Kenneth Frampton's call for unity between the abstractions of modernism and the particularities of *genius loci*, whilst, on the other, address the appeal in 'Building Scotland', the seminal manifesto written by architects Alan Reiach and Robert Hurd in 1944, for an approach that looked both to the best of European modernism and to the simplicity and common sense of a local vernacular.

The practice's early work accepted the budgetary exigencies inevitable in what was then an ultra-low-value economy but, through a resolute determination to develop the typology, managed to bring serious architectural merit to sometimes unprepossessing commissions. The continuing nature of these projects led to the practice developing a range of self-build options for people unable to afford a bespoke home but who wished the same highly-insulated, low-energy quality and well-tested details as found in Dualchas' award-winning projects. Subsequently, the practice formed an offshoot company—Heb Homes—to market and build these, a business diversification that has proved to be remarkably successful in helping to stem the tide of execrable kit houses referred to earlier. Initially based on timber frame construction, the houses are currently constructed from SIPs but may soon be fabricated from cross laminated timber, a development decision based in part upon the practice's desire to help create a bigger market for the production of this engineered timber product in Scotland from locally-grown timber.

It is Dualchas' one-off houses that have built the practice's reputation, however, and which—along with the work of Rural Design—have had a hugely influential effect, not only upon client perceptions of the architectural skill and quality available locally, but on an upcoming generation of architects who now see opportunity to work in Scotland after qualification and to find their own direction within the domestic environment, rather than follow the time-honoured student tradition of taking their talent south to London. Four houses—three in the north-west of the island and one closer to the Dualchas office in the south, give some indication of the practice's recent evolution and why it continues to attract attention and plaudits from critics. Common to each of these homes is the avoidance of the one feature that makes standard kit homes such a blight: whilst they are built high on the ground and all too visibly, the Dualchas' approach has been to follow a tradition that is also environmentally sensible: to tuck the houses into the landscape, sheltered as much as possible from the extremes of weather but making the most of the views out.

The first example, **Tigh Port na Long** (2011) sits near to the most southerly point of Skye, at Aird of Sleat, with views on three sides—across to the mainland peninsulas of Ardnamurchan and Knoydart, and down the coast to the island of Eigg. Built tight to the ground, the house has two distinct blocks derived from traditional long, narrow forms and connected by a small, service link. A step in the foundations corresponds to a slope in the landscape and gives

Borreraig,
Glendale, Isle of Skye (2011)
Dualchas
Photographer: Andrew Lee

166

additional height to the main living space in the front block, which, in its prime position on the site, has been provided with three terraces: one outside the kitchen to benefit from morning light; one from the dining space to enjoy afternoon light; and the third from the main bedroom to gain evening light. The house's simple, abstracted forms are deceptive: the larch rainscreen exhibits a level of design minimalism that belies its primary purpose—to shield the walls and flat roofs from strong wind and driving rain—and is the result of a process of detail refinement that has been developed through the practice's long experience gained in the construction of other houses similarly exposed to Skye's extremes of climate.

Sixty-five miles and an almost two hour drive to the north-west of the island is **Borreraig** (2011), a home with three constituent parts: the living accommodation, the bedroom wing and the studio, each of which has its own place in the hierarchy of the dwelling's built forms. Designed for a practising Buddhist, the brief was to create a calm, contemplative space to which the client could regularly escape from life in the city. A natural bowl in the landscape was transformed into a small loch by damming the outflowing burns (streams) to become the foreground for views from the house and to embed this quiet place with an even greater sense of serenity. The single-storey dwelling is partially shielded from the narrow road by a surrounding wall constructed of local stone. Internally, the house has a simple palette: Caithness stone that has been honed to a smooth finish for the floors; and oak-faced ply panels set out on a 600mm grid that line the walls and sloping ceilings. Only the freestanding kitchen pavilion that separates the living spaces from the study is finished with plaster. Externally, the practice's familiarity with the use of larch cladding can again be seen: horizontally-fixed and subtly layered, with heavily insulated shutters as a barrier to the worst of the gales, integrated within the thickness of the walls. The difference between this and other timber-clad houses in the area can be seen again in the sophistication of the detailing: there are no visible pipes or gutters; the corners of the walls are tightly mitred rather than encased in clumsy, vertical edge strips; and the junctions between the walls and the profiled, grey metal cladding of the roofs are expressed as thin lines. The walls have now weathered to a consistent grey to match the roof, allowing the forms of the house to sit quietly and harmoniously within the landscape, very much as if they have always been there.

Borreraig,
Glendale, Isle of Skye (2011)
Dualchas
Photographer: Andrew Lee

By way of contrast, **Colbost** (2012) sits nearby on an elevated croft site that has stunning views over Dunvegan Bay to the Waternish peninsula and, further still, to the Outer Hebridean Isle of Harris. Built for a family of five, the black-coloured house is made up of a pair of linear, pitched-roofed pavilions set parallel and slid lengthwise out of alignment, with a flat-roofed entrance hall forming the connection between the two. A garage and shed—also with pitched roofs—complete what appears from the road to be a cluster of low, agricultural buildings set around a tight, sheltered courtyard. The single-storey front pavilion, contains the communal, open plan living areas and enjoys the views; the rear contains the bedrooms, bathrooms and games room. This pavilion exhibits a characteristic common to much of the housing on Skye in being one-and-a-half storeys high and containing further sleeping areas within the roofspace. The front and back blocks both gain additional, natural light from above via a series of rooflights set into their rear roof planes and which are entirely unseen from the road. As with the previous two houses examined here, Colbost is highly insulated—260mm in the roof and 200mm in the walls—which, in combination with high-spec windows and an orientation designed to bring in solar warmth, has ensured that very little heating is required. Internally, the austere, but very stylish, monochrome palette of black floor and white walls and ceilings is offset by the warmth of the timber stair in the rear pavilion and the large oak sliding door that allows the living area to be separated completely from the bedroom zone. Externally, the Siberian larch clad walls are stained black to match the aluminium roof sheeting with its black Plannja Hard Coat finish. Colbost's forms, material and colour choices, together with the house's concealed gutters and downpipes and the practice's now almost standard flush detailing, stand in sharp counterpoint to the adjacent white-painted dwelling, the latter taking the role of farmhouse whilst the former reveals itself as a very modern interpretation of traditional agricultural volumes.

A mere four miles further north, on the same west side of Loch Dunvegan is the **Cliff House** (2014). The owners had looked at more than 100 plots and renovation possibilities before settling on the tucked-away site at Galtrigill. So hidden, in fact, was this piece of land, that the local planners insisted that the house should be kept so low as to only give a hint of a roof line to passers-by. The brief asked for a sea-facing home able to capture the panoramic views across the loch, but with further planning constraints that required the house to be constructed with natural materials that would meld into the landscape, the final form was

Colbost, Waternish, Isle of Skye (2012)
Dualchas
Photographer: Andrew Lee

**The Cliff House,
Galtrigill, Isle of Skye** (2014)
Dualchas
Photographer: Andrew Lee

predicated upon that found in the simple stone agricultural buildings that punctuate the surrounding area and which are cut into the ground to screen them from the wind. In the case of the Cliff House, a natural dip in the topography allowed a sheltered entrance to be formed in a recess in the building's stone-faced rear wall. This low-key approach to the property is entirely confounded by the drama that awaits the visitor once the threshold is crossed: a completely open-plan interior fronted by the end-to-end wall of Super low-E insulated glazing that provides the wide vista to wilder world beyond. The forms of the Cliff House are simple and bold, but were not entirely simple to construct in this location: its proximity to the edge of the cliff and the ferocity of the stormy weather in these parts meant the house had to be engineered in steel, an extra expense added to by the ground-workers hitting extremely hard rock when digging the foundations, a problem that added several weeks to the construction programme. Internally, clerestory glazing runs the full length of the building, bringing light into the corridor that separates the externally-expressed rear bedrooms from the living area; the kitchen is recessed into a third, stone-clad rear block that is additionally lit over the worktops by a row of top-lights in its flat roof. Externally, the front and side walls of the living area are clad with Scotlarch®, a name trademarked by local supplier, Russwood, that authenticates the material as timber grown in the Scottish Highlands.

Several of the houses by the other practice featured in this chapter may be familiar to readers schooled over the years by Kevin McCloud in some of the more unusual residential buildings constructed in the UK. The projects that Rural Design creates on the Isle of Skye are distinctive rather than idiosyncratic, however, and are very much founded in the landscape, construction practices and economic imperatives of this part of the country. Indeed, some its most widely published houses have also had the lowest budgets—not only for Skye, but for the UK as a whole. Producing houses that are affordable has not only been a business reality for much of this practice's life, but something of a moral and social commitment to sustaining communities and employment on the island.

The earliest of the projects to generate widespread interest was the 70 sq/m **Hen House** (2010), set within the wild landscape at Fiskavaig, a crofting settlement on the island's west coast Minginish peninsula. Originally intended to be a holiday house for clients from the Midlands, the experience of using the compact, two-bedroom, trapezoidal structure convinced the couple to spend the bulk of their time there. In part, this decision was prompted by the views across the area's wilderness landscape, but the architects' initial reaction to the undulating humps of the site was not to build on ground that had been untouched for millions of years. To mitigate against more serious intervention, the design ultimately produced for the lean-to like, wedge-shaped building has raised it above the ground on stilts, with a timber ramp leading to its recessed entrance. Ordinarily, the convention is to avoid north facing windows but, this being the direction of the best views from the Hen House, the decision was made to locate the principal glazed gable on this side. Other views from the property have been carefully thought out, with the slot windows on the west elevation arranged to afford glimpses of two curious, flat-topped hills known as Macleod's Tables. A large, south-facing first floor window heats the super-insulated, airtight home very effectively. The Hen House is, in fact, more eco-minimal than eco-tech, relying on passive approaches to provide its energy needs instead of the heat pumps, wind turbines and photovoltaic panels that, in some quarters, are disparagingly referred to as eco-bling. This disregard for convention extends to the internal wall and ceiling linings, where Oriented Strand Board (OSB), a relatively inexpensive panel product that is rarely seen in uncovered form in finished houses, has been used throughout, albeit carefully cut and fixed by the joiner once he learned it was to be the finished surface. Externally, the asymmetrical timber framed house has vertically-fixed larch cladding, except on the projecting ground floor w.c., where the material has been installed horizontally. Completing the Hen House's allusion to the area's ubiquitous farm buildings, the roof is sheeted with corrugated, glass fibre cement panels.

Fiskavaig, Isle of Skye (2010)
Rural Design
Photographer: Andrew Lee

Turf House,
Kendram, Isle of Skye (2012)
Rural Design
Photographer: Nigel Rigden

A similar aesthetic was applied to the eponymously-roofed **Turf House** (2012), at Kendram on the Trotternish peninsula and close to the most northerly point of the island. The clients here not only wanted to be "part of the place" they wanted their home to sit within the landscape rather than stand on it and, with the terrain here being relatively flat, the building, together with its adjacent studio, is set low on the seaward side of the road to minimise its visual impact. Just as—if not more,—importantly, this bedding down into the land has been an important design move to help protect the house from the extremes of weather in this very exposed location. This latter factor ensured the need for large steel portal frames to be bedded into the house's concrete base in order to provide strength and stability (racking performance, in structural engineer-speak) to the 200mm deep timber frame that forms its unusual lozenge shape. Being just 9° south of the Arctic Circle, the climate at this end of the Isle of Skye is often one of heavy rain, horizontally-driven by fierce winds of up to 120mph (193km/h). In response, high levels of insulation and airtightness were required for the 90 sq/m Turf House, not only within the fabric abut also in its glass doors and windows. In this context, the client stipulation that the house should have a turf roof has been beneficial in two other respects: it has added weight to the structure and has provided an extra level of insulation to the building. The walls have been clad vertically with Scotlarch® fixed board-on-board, as much for the architects' desire that the house's appearance should be an honest reflection of the timber technology that forms its structure, as for the many environmental benefits associated with the use of wood in construction. The end result is unequivocal: the Turf House is very much of its place and time, its design having drawn on traditional, almost primitive, forms to deliver an affordable modern house that could not easily be envisaged in any other location.

R.HOUSE
Rural Design with James MacQueen Builders
Photographer: Nigel Rigden

R.HOUSE
Rural Design with James
MacQueen Builders
Photographer: Nigel Rigden

Rural Design has, over the years of the practice's existence, designed many homes, but the pressing need for affordable accommodation for people—especially young families—living close to its office led to the development of a range of prefabricated house types that could be manufactured locally and quickly assembled on site, a long-standing requirement for house building in all parts of Scotland, where the imperative has always been to erect the walls and roof quickly before the weather changes. In 2011, the practice formed a joint venture company with James MacQueen Building Contractors Ltd, a local company it had long worked with and whose skills and experience it respected and trusted. The resulting **R.HOUSE** product is now fabricated in a large workshop on the west side of the island—an indigenous, highly adaptable product that offers a contemporary response to the paradox posited by Kenneth Frampton in the 1980s: the R.HOUSE convincingly demonstrates that it is possible simultaneously to become modern and to return to sources.

Heb Homes
Dualchas
Photographer: Dualchas

Paralleled by Dualchas' **Heb Homes** initiative, as well as by the day-to-day work of both practices, the architectural landscape of the Isle of Skye has, over the past two decades, been transformed from anonymous mediocrity into something that has its own distinctive, indigenous quality. The quiet influence of these endeavours is also increasingly being seen in excellent projects on other Inner and Outer Hebridean islands and on nearby mainland areas: a definitive and sustainable, regional modern architecture is finding wider expression through the work of a new generation of architects.

An outstanding example of this is the **House at Camusdarrach Sands** (2013), by Raw Architecture Workshop, located on the mainland, just south of the estuary of the River Morar and across the water from the Aird of Sleat, the southern tip of the Isle of Skye. Built on a steep slope formerly used for rough grazing, the part-subterranean house has a skewed plan and inverted section, with the living spaces located on its uppermost level and the bedrooms and entry floors layered beneath. Access at the lowest of the houses three levels leads into an entrance hall in the building's reinforced concrete base as well as to a boat room and spare bedroom. A birch ply staircase rises from here up to a second level containing three bedrooms. The top level houses an open plan living space, kitchen and dining area, each benefitting from increased daylight and taller ceilings. The construction was carried out by a local house- and boat-building firm and is deliberately of low-tech construction: an exposed concrete base supporting a timber frame superstructure clad with black-painted, slow-grown cedar sourced from a Forestry Commission Scotland less than 50 miles away. The timber structure in the top floor of this unusually shaped dwelling was formed from a series of deep ribs with V-shaped ply gussets fixed on either side to connect opposing rafters and studs and ensure that no structural bracing would be visible. The design draws on the simple gabled form of traditional Highland dwellings, but in twisting the plan, views from the house are directed from the widened gables towards, at one end, the mountains and, at the other, out to the islands. A more complex structure, perhaps, than the others highlighted in this chapter but, like them, the House at Camusdarrach Sands captures the spirit of its location and which brings a distinctive, sustainable quality to this remote part of Scotland.

Camusdarrach Sands (2013)
Raw Architecture Workshop
Photographer: David Barbour

Chapter 11
The Hybrid Timber House

In all of the applications of timber in the construction of houses so far identified in this book, one group of new dwellings defies simple categorisation. This comprises the houses in which timber plays an important complementary role to the other materials employed and is neither dominant nor applied as decoration or affectation. In such instances, each material is part of the house's fundamental conception and central to the design ethos, having been selected for their ability to form a harmonious relationship with its neighbour(s). The use of timber is not, therefore, in the form of an addition to a building, nor is it of the structural hybrid type in which it may be combined with steel or concrete to provide a more efficient structural solution as in, for example, the Cube at Banyan Wharf (see chapter 12, The Tall Timber House). The houses highlighted here are predominantly rural and where the choice of materials has been prompted by local environmental conditions, planning constraints and/or the desire to respond to the vernacular building traditions, techniques and materials of the area. In each case, the result has been, *de facto*, to create a contemporary home that interacts positively with its immediate landscape: a material hybrid rather than one of structure, in which the contribution of the timber or timber product is integral to the building's sense of place.

This definition of hybrid timber construction can be seen at its simplest in the **Strathdon House** (2016) by Brown + Brown Architects. Located within the boundaries of the Cairngorms National Park at Newe in the Strathdon area of Aberdeenshire, this modest budget, single-storey, two-bedroom home takes its design cue from the site's topography, its rear wall being positioned tightly against the wooded area that forms the northern edge of the plot, with views towards the River Don to the south. This north wall is designed to be a thermal store and is constructed in blockwork with a 300mm insulated cavity, clad inside and out with prefabricated stacked slate panels. The wall rises to a datum forming the cill of a high-performance clerestory window that runs continuously around three sides of the house. Outside, waist-high stacked slate walls continue the line of this edge of the building to the east and west, rooting it to its site and acting as a barrier to the trees beyond as well as concealing the rear driveway entrance to the north-east of the house and its hardstanding parking area. A prefabricated cladding panel of the same slate punctuates the south elevation, breaking this facade's alternating rhythm of larch cladding and full-height picture windows.

It is this external timber rainscreen cladding that provides the Strathdon House with one of its two most characteristic visual features, the other being its monopitch, standing-seam grey metal roof, the incline of which is angled to echo the southward slope of the site. The Siberian larch cladding is untreated and fixed to allow an 8mm shadow and ventilation gap between each horizontal board. The boards themselves are chamfered at 45° on their top and bottom edges, with black building paper behind to conceal the oversized 150mm battens needed to provide a large enough cavity to conceal the house's rainwater downpipes. The walls behind

**Sweethaws,
Redbridge Lane,
Sweethaws Wood,
East Sussex** (2013)
Smerin Architects
Photographer: Tim Crocker

**Strathdon House,
Cairngorms National Park,
Newe, Strathdon,
Aberdeenshire** (2016)

Brown + Brown Architects

Photography: Brown + Brown
Architects

are formed from prefabricated timber cassettes, concealing the uprights to the steel portal frames that support the heavily insulated roof.

The Strathdon House's very efficient linear plan and construction belies the depth of thinking that has gone into making this dwelling as self-sufficient in energy terms as possible. The house requires very little heating and is, to all intents and purposes, built to Passivhaus standards. Delivering this, whilst responding to the exacting planning conditions pertaining within the Cairngorms National Park is no mean feat and an achievement recognised by the Authority in its 2016 Design Awards: not only was the Strathdon House the winner of the 'Best House' category, it secured the 'Overall Winner' prize too. The house's ability to sit within its immediate environment as if it has grown out of the landscape and the local material resource, is possibly a more valuable testament to the decision to employ a hybrid construction approach and for timber to play an equal part in the palette of materials used.

Moving from a single-storey to a two-storey example, the **Broad Street House** (2014), by Nash Baker Architects, sits in the Suffolk coastal village of Orford. The site is relatively flat but at risk of tidal flooding, a condition that premised the decision to build the 200 sq/m house on a raised concrete beam and block plinth. This was constructed within the floor plate constraints of a previous, incongruous house dating from the 1980's that was demolished to create a new home, able to take advantage of the quality of natural light in the area and of the views across the marshes to Orford Ness and the coast beyond.

The clients' brief, in this instance, was for an exceptional contemporary home that would nevertheless be sympathetic to its neighbouring properties. In addition, an open-plan arrangement at ground floor had to accommodate dedicated work rooms for their respective professional activities as baker and silversmith, together with the normal domestic zones of kitchen, dining and living. This level of the house is thus delineated quite separately from the upstairs' functions, its traditional cavity wall construction making use of locally-sourced handmade bricks which, to create a more distinctive appearance, were laid in a variation of 'Monk's Bond', a configuration that requires every two stretcher (S) bricks to be met with a header (H) brick (-H-SS-H-SS-H-) and each course offset to allow the headers to be vertically aligned. White iron-free sand was also mixed with lime from the local Wivenhoe pit to create the mortar joints.

The head of the wall sees the same bricks laid vertically to form a continuous coping which is met by a complete change of material to the house's first floor. Here, the precision of the bricklaying is emulated by untreated oak cladding in which each vertical board has been sized to match the brick course dimensions, with a series of tall openings, two boards wide, providing light to the first floor stair landing. The open-jointed oak boards continue as a rainscreen

**Broad Street House,
Orford, Suffolk** (2015)

Nash Baker Architects

Photography: Nick Gutteridge

over the pitched roof to the rear elevation where, again laid vertically, they form a frame to the recessed continuous glazing of the house's master bedroom suite. It is at the front of the house, however, where the relationship created between bricks and timber is at its most harmonious: a ground floor panel of untreated oak with the same two-board vertical gaps for glazing distinguishing the entrance within the crisp brickwork frame. Directly above, a large, square window defines the house's second bedroom whilst also emphasising the elegant asymmetry of the facade's overall composition. The ambition to blend with the architectural character of the village has been more than met here by the house's assured design and construction, the clean aesthetic of which is continued inside with floors of whitewashed Douglas fir planks and fitted joinery made from lacquered, birch-faced plywood.

Some 80 miles north, **The Arboretum** (2014), by Cowper Griffith Architects, is built on a large wooded site in the centre of a Norfolk seaside village. The coastal site rises steeply from the shoreline at its north-eastern end to elevated ground to the south-west where valuable woodland mitigated against it being included in the development. In designing the house, the architects have chosen, therefore, to situate its essentially linear form at the shore end of the plot, parallel to the sea and perpendicular to this incline. This stratagem, whilst partially setting The Arboretum within the North Sea Flood Zone, also permitted its length to be cut into the land rising crossways on the site and enabling the entire ground level to be located above the maximum anticipated flood point. Below this, excavation has created sufficient space for a boat store, accessed from the garage that sits beneath the master bedroom suite in a central wing projecting towards the coast. Adjacent to this, an undercroft offers covered space for more cars as well as the house's fully-glazed entrance box, the stair within which leads, initially, to the ground floor, bedroom level of the house.

There is no question that The Arboretum is a large house: the accommodation provides for a family with three teenage sons and frequent guests, necessitating an entire floor comprised of six bedrooms and two studies plus plant and utility rooms. Arriving from the entrance to this cellular level leaves the visitor unprepared for the culmination of the next stage in the

The Arboretum, North Norfolk coast (2014)
Cowper Griffiths Architects
Photographer: Peter Cook

ascent: the dark oak stair treads to the first floor of the house lead directly into a comfortably-sized and naturally-lit living area set between a bookcase room divider, concealing a smaller television zone and a double-aspect freestanding fireplace block that services both it and the dining area. The north-east face of the living areas is fully glazed, whilst the opposite side of this elongated, open-plan kitchen/dining/living space opens onto a continuous seated balcony accessed via full-height, sliding glazed units and with views to the trees at the south-west end of the site.

The hybrid structural steel frame and concrete floor slabs within this house are largely unseen, the former contained within the build up of the walls, the latter hidden beneath wide timber boards. It is the exterior that provides The Arboretum with its exemplar material hybrid credentials: the projecting north-east wing is finished in coursed flint-work that extends through the undercroft entrance level to reappear along the right-hand end of the south-west, ground floor elevation. A series of identical glazed doors, opening onto an external deck, signifies three of the bedrooms, with doors to two other room-height openings indicating, at the left, an entrance through a storage area and, to the right, a staircase concealed behind the flint-work and which rises to the first floor balcony.

To the left of the projecting flint-work elevation, the house extends out from the land, the floor forming the soffit of the undercroft and providing the lower datum for the vertical timber cladding which rises to meet a metal channel separating it from the wider boards that face the first floor level. On the north-east side of the house, the elevation is almost entirely clad with vertical timber boards, the ground and first floors again are separated by a metal channel between the two levels.

In a maritime environment such as this, the air is moist with salt and demands the use of materials resistant to deterioration and fungal decay. Flint-work is the traditional, locally-available material in this part of England: tried, tested, resilient and responsive in its colouring to the natural light of the area. The use of timber in the conditions prevailing here, however, demands that the species selected should be able to withstand wind, rain and sea moisture over a long period of time and, to meet these criteria, the architects selected a less well-known, but extremely durable hardwood, Louro Vermehlo, a species found in central and southern America but largely sourced from Brazil, and which is more commonly used for ship's decking and bridges. Sometimes known as Red Louro, the wood is light brown with pink to red shades that, at the Arboretum, marry well with the house's red zinc standing-seam roofing. The relationship between the timber cladding and the flint-work is synergistic: the slowly weathering Louro providing a warm, dark contrast to the brightly reflective surfaces of the flint-work. This is a house very much of its place and time, its hybrid combination of crisply detailed external materials more than amply justifying its selection by the RIBA East region as its 'Building of the Year' in 2014.

Moving away from coastal projects to the more pastoral landscape that surrounds Sweethaws Wood in East Sussex, the house now known as **Sweethaws** (2013) is situated some three miles or so from Crowborough in East Sussex. This 22-acre estate of protected woodland was once connected to Ashdown Forest in the Weald and is reached via Redbridge Lane, a twisting single-track road bounded on either side by tall hedges separating it from the rolling fields that now surround Sweethaws Wood. The root of the names for both the lane and the Red Bridge House (the title by which this project was originally known) are to be found in the locality's soil and network of streams: iron-rich, the colouring in the landscape here was also been an important influence on the selection of materials used on the house's exterior. Designed by Smerin Architects, this three-storey structure replaced a plywood summerhouse built by the estate's owners in the 1920s that, by the time the site was purchased in 2009, had become almost derelict and the surrounding garden, pond and wood largely overgrown.

**The Arboretum,
North Norfolk coast** (2014)
Cowper Griffiths Architects
Photographer: Peter Cook

Into this neglected landscape stepped new owners who wished to demolish the decaying building and replace it with a home for their family of five, an aspiration acceded to by the local planners, providing that their design proposals would situate the house on the footprint of its predecessor and be accompanied by a woodland management plan for the larger site. The stipulated plot has a drop of three metres from front to back, a topographical condition that helped to orchestrate the house's accommodation: approached frontally on its elongated north-west face, the impression is of a flat-roofed two-storey dwelling, its lower ground floor being set into the site and largely invisible at this point. Attention, in any case, is more on the materiality of the building's facade and of the bridge leading to the house's entrance: Corten is the generic name given to a group of steel alloys developed to eliminate the need for painting and which form a stable rust-like appearance when exposed to the weather over a length of time. Nowadays, the material can be supplied in pre-weathered form and, in this location, its orange-tinged surface very obviously complements the hues of the landscape it faces onto.

The choice of material for the other three elevations to the house is very different. Looking back at Sweethaws from the bottom of the slope, the house appears as a continuous plate that has been folded twice to turn the ground floor through 90° to form the north-east facade and then turn it again to become the roof. This end elevation is clad from ground level to roof with vertically-fixed Thermowood®, a very durable modified timber (see chapter 4), its surface interrupted only by two very large, asymmetrically-placed and flush-mounted windows. From this viewpoint, the glazed exterior of the lower ground level of the house is visible beneath the exposed soffit of the ground floor's reinforced concrete slab which is cantilevered outwards to form a wide, building-length balcony. Above, the roof has a similarly wide cantilever, with 15mm diameter tensed steel rods dropping from its soffit to bring additional support to the balcony deck. Set back from this six metre-high covered balcony, the south-east facade of the house stands as a well-proportioned balance of the same timber cladding and storey-height triple-glazed window units. In turn, the south-west facade is an almost solid plane of vertically fixed Thermowood®, pierced only by a single door that leads onto the wraparound balcony.

**Sweethaws,
Redbridge Lane,
Sweethaws Wood,
East Sussex** (2013)

Smerin Architects
Photographer: Tim Crocker

The choice of external materials for Sweethaws is instructive: originally the architects had hoped to clad the building in timber sourced from trees in the surrounding woods, but the cost of processing, drying and treating the raw material proved to be prohibitive (although locally sourced oak has been used for the internal stair). The decision instead to use thermally modified timber, a premium product, to clad three sides of the house has had a number of benefits, not the least being the material's dependable extended durability. The modification process also tends to darken the host species which, in turn, can minimise the often unsightly effects of differential weathering. In this case, the darkened wood has tied the building to its immediate context in the homogeneous relationship that has been created with the surrounding trees. This, and its harmonious colour balance with the north-west elevation's Corten surface has produced a material hybrid classic.

Steambent House, Cornwall (2016)
Tom Raffield
Photographer: Kirstin Prisk

Like the other houses in this chapter, the final example, **Nanskerro**, otherwise known as Steambent House (2016), is also to be found in a rural location: so much so that the bulk of the materials used in its construction came from within the six acres (2.43 hectares) of ancient woodland that surrounds it. The house's hybrid nature differs from them, however, in two very distinct ways: it is actually an extension to the Grade II listed, stone-built gamekeeper's lodge dating from 1882, albeit that the addition is four times the size of its host building; and because it makes very deliberate hybrid use of several different timber species in its construction. Located within the Trevarno Estate in Cornwall, the enlarged dwelling is home to furniture designers/makers Tom and Danielle Raffield, who specialise in the use of steam-bending techniques to create their own range of contemporary products from locally-grown wood. The lodge had been their home for three years but, not only was it cramped and mouldy with few mod cons (the toilet and bathroom were on the other side of a courtyard), the Raffield's and their two children had completely outgrown its 44 sq/m living space.

Having only a very small budget to work with, the couple engaged local architectural technologist, Chris Strike of RA Design, to develop a timber frame structure in accord with their design ideas for the house. The frame needed to be built on site by two local joiners, a not entirely straightforward proposition since the house was to be set into the side of a hill adjacent to the existing stone toilet block. This, seemingly simple, idea necessitated the lengthy task of removing 3000 tonnes of earth before retaining the sides of the newly-formed niche with earth-filled tyres and gabion baskets.

Once constructed, the frame became the canvas for an extraordinarily artistic exercise in external timber cladding: the house, as completed, is entirely covered in horizontally-fixed, open-jointed lengths of curving beech, larch, sweet chestnut and oak collected from the surrounding woodland, an approach that not only kept costs down but which fulfilled the couple's desire for their house to "fit with the contours of the land and blend in." The pièce de résistance and the element that umbilically connects the extension to the older building is the section of cladding that, made up of strips of steam-bent ash and oak turns at head height from the (now) larger part of the house across the stone surface before curling outwards and then curving down before twisting again to create a seemingly suspended horizontal bench against the wall. The other end of this floating seat then turns upwards again before twisting at right angles—once to return the five cladding strips towards the wall—and twice to turn again to form the fascia above the timber framed windows and cladding of the link between the old house and the addition.

This masterly use of wood has rightly brought widespread recognition (initiated by Grand Designs) to Nanskerro's owners who, by using locally-found material and carrying out much of the work themselves, managed to contain the cost of this remarkable dwelling to within £160,000 at 2016 prices.

The Hybrid Timber House, then, far from being the curate's egg of the timber design and construction world, can be seen to offer far more to the breadth of modern timber architecture than the all-too-common application of a few, gratuitous panels of external cladding appearing as fashion items on many of the country's conventional housing developments. In all of the projects featured here, the materials employed can be seen to have been skilfully balanced, with the creative use of wood playing an integral part in the overall success of each design.

Steambent House, Cornwall (2016)
Tom Raffield
Photographer: Kirstin Prisk

190

Chapter 12
The Tall Timber House

The emergence of modern engineered wood products, especially cross laminated timber (CLT), has unquestionably altered the way in which architects and engineers now consider the design and construction of tall residential buildings. This, together with rapidly changing demographics and the limited availability of land in denser urban areas, has resulted in something of a revolution in inner city housing and one in which the UK—or more particularly, London—currently leads the world.

Many of the reasons why CLT—alone, or in combination with other laminated timber products, as well as in hybrid form with non-timber materials—has stimulated new thinking amongst architects and engineers about the potential of solid timber in residential construction were articulated in Chapter 3 – The Solid Timber House. The beginnings of this reappraisal of timber as a material suitable for use in the design of tall structures can be easily dated to the completion of the **Stadthaus** (2008) in the London Borough of Hackney, prior to which the development of timber construction in UK housing was predominantly based upon platform frame technology, a construction method generally considered to be effective up to seven storeys in height. The Stadthaus's eight storeys of cross laminated timber above a single storey reinforced concrete plinth effectively removed this limitation on tall timber buildings forever.

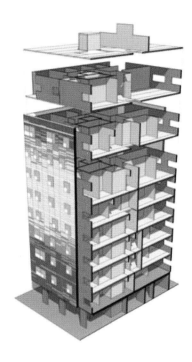

Diagram of Stadthaus honeycomb structure

**Stadthaus,
Murray Grove,
London Borough of Hackney**
(2008)

Waugh Thistleton Architects

Designed by Waugh Thistleton Architects and Techniker engineers, this new approach to multi-storey residential building in a heavily built-up part of London ticked many boxes for the local authority, not the least being its outstanding carbon credentials. Speed of erection, reduced deliveries, minimal on-site waste and low noise generated during construction all added to the attractions of this approach and Hackney has since become something of a world epicentre for tall residential buildings formed from cross laminated timber, even to the point in 2012 when its Council considered introducing a 'Timber First' policy for new developments in the Borough (a radical proposition subsequently dropped due to intense opposition from other parts of the construction industry). The majority of timber towers constructed in London to date are within the eight to ten storey range, but the fact that they are there at all—in a city where the local Building Acts are predicated on the Great Fire of 1666—is testament to how far the product has come in a relatively short period of time, an observation confirmed elsewhere by the sheer number of tall residential CLT structures currently being built, or proposed, in cities around the globe.

**The Cube,
Banyan Wharf, London** (2015)

Wenlock Road,
London Borough of Hackney

Hawkins\Brown Architects

Photographer: Jack Hobhouse

The Stadthaus itself stands on a 17m x 17m plot, confined on all sides by pre-existing residential buildings, a factor in its overall height being restricted to nine storeys. A design complication introduced by the developer was the need to distinguish the five upper storeys from the three lower ones as the former were to be offered for private sale and the latter assigned as affordable social housing units. This mixed-tenure arrangement resulted in two separate ground floor entrances, each with its own lift and stair enclosure formed from solid timber and which, with the floors and load-bearing walls also being made of CLT (from Austrian manufacturer KLH), gave the building the distinction of being the first to be constructed in this way. It also demonstrated an entirely new and extremely efficient approach to the construction of housing in dense inner city areas: the 29 apartment (in one, two, three and four-bedroom units) Stadthaus was completed in its entirety within budget and on time within 49 weeks. Four carpenters assembled the CLT floors, walls and roof in a mere 27 days (three days per week for nine weeks). The panels' honeycomb arrangement was conceived to ensure the kind of progressive structural collapse that has haunted the construction of tall buildings in London since the Ronan Point disaster of 1968 cannot happen with this new timber technology. By developing the panelised system to be load-bearing throughout the building's height introduced other opportunities too: any of its internal walls could have a significant proportion of its area removed during factory production to provide door and other openings. This offered a design flexibility that easily allowed for different plan and fenestration arrangements: a benefit reflected in the orchestration of the 5000 Eternit panels (manufactured from 70% waste timber) that make up the building's facades.

The architects have calculated that the 90 cu/m of solid timber which makes up the structure of the Stadthaus has effectively sequestered 194 tonnes of carbon for the duration of the building's life; a substantial contribution to lowering the building's carbon footprint and a compelling factor in securing local authority approval for its construction.

Within a short walk of the Stadthaus, **Bridport House** (2011) sits within Hackney's Colville Estate and is an east-west oriented urban block comprised of two large building masses—one of eight storeys and the other of five. The development replaced an existing, five storey, 20-

Stadthaus,
Murray Grove,
London Borough of Hackney
(2008)
Waugh Thistleton Architects
Photographer: Will Pryce

unit concrete structure of the same name, built in the 1960s. A key design requirement for the new Bridport House was that it should contain twice the number of units (41 socially-rented dwellings) but be no more than 10% heavier than its predecessor. This weight restriction directly related to the existence of one of London's largest storm sewers immediately below the site, a factor that severely restricted the location of building foundations and piles. The extremely tight project timescale (two years from commissioning to completion) and the need to avoid months of negotiation with the private sector utilities provider, Thames Water, as well as potentially lengthy testing of alternative building technologies that could have jeopardised the availability of public funding from the Homes and Communities Agency, mitigated in favour of the lighter weight of CLT construction. In the interests of greater precision and construction efficiency, the panels were delivered to site pre-fitted with natural fibre insulation and servicing ducts and fully erected in only 10 weeks.

Unusually for such a large urban block, the design of the new Bridport House has delivered a coherent street frontage consisting of two main entrances to the flats above and eight front doors to the four-bedroom maisonettes that occupy the ground and first floor levels. The upper levels contain 33 one-, two- and three-bedroom apartments, each with floor to ceiling windows and external balconies cantilevered out some 2.5m and braced with angled tensile rods.

Bridport House,
London Borough of Hackney
(2011)
Karakusevic Carson Architects
Photographer: Ioana Marinescu

The brick cladding of the resulting building disguises the fact that the entire structure is formed from CLT (manufactured in Austria by Stora Enso), but here Karakusevic Carson Architects' competition-winning design employs this solid wood product in a quite different structural arrangement to that developed at Murray Grove. The structural innovation at Bridport House

Bridport House, London Borough of Hackney (2011)
Karakusevic Carson Architects
Photographer: Ioana Marinescu

is the 90 degree shift of loadbearing CLT panels from the two storey ground floor maisonettes to the single storey apartments above. Timber design usually demands that loads follow a continuous vertical path but here the loads have been shifted in support of the architectural and interior requirements. In order to achieve this, the structural engineers, Peter Brett Associates, working closely with suppliers/timber engineers Eurban, designed the CLT internal walls above the maisonettes to act as beams supported by the cross walls running at right angles from ground to second floor. This shift in the structural arrangements allows flexibility in the internal layouts since the exterior, corridor and party walls provide the main load-bearing elements at these levels. Three-storey high CLT panels were used to form the elevator shafts which, due to the precision of their manufacture, made the lift installation a simpler task than would have been the case in a conventional in-situ reinforced concrete core. This also removed the potential for differential movement between materials and any consequent requirement for more complex connection detailing.

Still within the London Borough of Hackney, Waugh Thistleton architects next foray into CLT construction (following their pioneering use of it in the Stadthaus) demonstrates not only the practice's confidence in the product but also their ability to use it creatively in a project for which they were the developer. The mixed-use building can be found at the end of Whitmore Road, a five-minute stroll from Bridport House and sited adjacent to the Whitmore Bridge over the Regent's Canal. A mere seven storeys in height, the **Whitmore Road** building (2012) is certainly not the highest of the tall timber developments in the area but, as with the two projects already discussed, it provided the opportunity to explore yet another approach to maximising the structural capabilities of this form of prefabricated timber panel.

In this instance, the site is tightly enclosed on its east and south sides by buildings, by the road/bridge to the west and the canal to the north; constraints that have informed the vertical disposition of spaces within the building and the structural arrangement of the floor and wall panels. The ground floor is formed in reinforced concrete to provide the base for the solid

Whitmore Road,
London Borough of Hackney
(2012)
Waugh Thistleton Architects
Photographer: Will Pryce / Waugh
Thistleton Architects

**The Cube,
Banyan Wharf, London** (2015)
Wenlock Road,
London Borough of Hackney
Hawkins\Brown Architects
Photographer: Jack Hobhouse

timber panel structure above. Offices here and on the level above look out onto the canal, with the CLT dividing walls and floor panels at first floor level not only spanning front-to-back but also cantilevering over the canal towpath to support the open-plan photographer's studio above. At the second and third floor level, the structural arrangement turns through 90 degrees, with the CLT panels here forming the external walls to this double height space and effectively acting as longitudinal beams, allowing the 9m x 23m room thus created to be entirely free of internal walls and columns. Above this—from the fifth to the seventh levels—are three-bedroom apartments, the CLT party walls between which once again span front-to-back, this time fulfilling the function of trusses.

The building is horizontally-clad with 120mm x 20mm sweet chestnut boards, a UK-grown hardwood, the heartwood of which is classified as durable and thus suitable for external use without preservative treatment or a water-repellant coating. The boards have been cut lengthwise in order that their ends align with the orchestration of the window openings in the facade. Each board is profiled to allow water to run off the surface and spaced to allow air to move around the timber via the ventilated cavity behind to ensure quicker drying. Aside from its reinforced concrete ground floor and piled foundations, the Whitmore Road building is therefore predominantly formed from timber, 499 cu/m of which is comprised of structural CLT (equating to 108 tonnes of sequestered carbon) erected in five weeks by a four-man team.

Continuing to follow the circuit of Hackney's growing number of tall timber buildings, a further 10 minutes walk from Whitmore Road leads to Wenlock Road, where architects Hawkins\Brown have pushed the structural use of CLT into hybrid territory. Their design for '**The Cube**' at Banyan Wharf (2015) is a complex arrangement of floor plates rotated 25.5 degrees on every alternate level, an arrangement that, for structural efficiency, required the solid wood floor and wall panels to be combined with a steel frame and a reinforced concrete core. The 10-storey project contains 50 one-, two- and three-bedroom apartments (between four and six per floor), each of which—due to the twisting plan arrangement of the floor plates—benefits from having three external walls (meaning that all flats are dual- or triple-aspect corner units). This strategy allows for full cross ventilation and excellent daylighting to every flat as well as providing spacious external terraces with views along the Wenlock Basin or across the park to the east.

Achieving all this plus the creation of courtyards on all four corners of the tight urban plot necessitated some quite unusual constructional gymnastics: essentially cruciform in plan, the floors, external walls and roofs of the Cube are formed from CLT, the gravitational load of which is supported by a steel frame. The frame transfers these forces into the skewed plates of the alternate floors which, acting as diaphragms within the overall structural design, facilitate the load path from the facades to the central reinforced concrete core.

Despite its structural complexity, the building ably demonstrates a number of CLT's positive attributes and why its use has been fundamental to the development of the design in this instance. Being manufactured in factory conditions and with all openings pre-cut, the panels—around four tonnes in weight and up to 200mm thick—are dimensionally very accurate and stable and—at 12m end-to-end—corresponded to the entire length of the structure, ensuring that not only could they be raised straight into position from the transportation vehicles as they arrived, but that the number of actual lifts was minimised, important considerations given the project's proximity to adjacent properties and the usual restrictions on the number and timings of deliveries (in this instance there was only room for one trailer or van delivery at a time).

Given that a building of this height is predominantly clad in timber and has floors walls and roof of the same material, the issue of fire protection inevitably looms large from the earliest design stages. Whilst many misconceptions still remain amongst construction professionals and public alike about the fire performance of timber in tall structures, as a solid timber product CLT is inherently stable when subjected to high temperatures. The surfaces of solid timber panels char during combustion, but this char zone can be calculated from readily available tables and added to the dimensions necessary to ensure structural integrity. Once charring is complete, no further burning takes place and the panels retain their strength and stiffness. As B&K Structures, the highly experienced specialist structural contractor for the Banyan Wharf project, has pointed out, "CLT is the only structural timber solution to fully comply with all Fire Resistance REI classes (loadbearing capacity, structural integrity and insulation) and

Dalston Lane,
London Borough of Hackney
(2017)
Waugh Thistleton Architects
Photographer: Waugh Thistleton

Dalston Lane,
London Borough of Hackney
(2017)
Waugh Thistleton Architects
Photographer: Daniel Shearing

performance requirements without any need for costly add-ons, build-ups or adaptations": credentials that have contributed to the company's confidence to "provide assurances to the lending community that the structure will deliver a consistent performance over a determined durability of 60 years."

Fire is not the only challenge to be confronted when designing multi-unit residential structures: acoustic and thermal performance are two of the leading complaints from occupants, no matter what construction system has been employed. Taking each of these issues in turn, a great deal of research has been focused on the control of sound transmission in solid timber structures in order to develop details that fully address noise transmitted either through the air or via the building structure itself (e.g. footsteps on laminated flooring). In the case of the Cube at Banyan Wharf, the architects elected to have one of the apartments completed on an accelerated programme in order to test the adequacy of the specified sound and thermal insulation provision before proceeding to construct the other flats. These tests enabled the internal linings to be adjusted to meet the overall performance criteria established for the building with, for example, an additional insulation layer introduced under the flooring to assist with heat retention in each of the flats.

The largest of the projects to be found in Hackney—and undoubtedly the most ambitious to date in urban design terms—sits at **Dalston Lane** (2017), a little way north of the buildings examined so far. With over 12,500 sq/m of residential floor area and 3,460 sq/m of commercial space, the 10-storey, 121-unit development for the private rented sector is constructed from 4,693 cu/m of cross laminated timber and currently lays claim to being the largest CLT structure by volume in the world. Commissioned by the same developer (Regal Homes) as the Banyan Wharf project, the architects for this project are again Waugh Thistleton, arguably now pre-eminent amongst UK exponents of the use of CLT in the construction of tall residential buildings and unashamed in their determination "to roll out the use of timber in high-density urban housing in London and beyond."

Working with timber engineering specialists, Ramboll, the project's authors have been vocal in extolling the very significant carbon benefits that underpin the design of this development. With CLT forming the external, party and core walls as well as all floors and stairs, the team has calculated that the overall building comprises a mere 21.5% of the weight of an equivalent size reinforced concrete structure (2,300 tonnes instead of 10,700 tonnes), with a commensurate reduction in deliveries to site of some 84%. This vastly reduced weight has had the very direct benefit of making it possible to construct a significantly taller building than would otherwise have been possible on what was previously a blighted brownfield area of land.

In considering the site's potential to make a positive contribution to the continuing regeneration of the area, the architects have designed this brick-clad project as two distinct but connected masses, varying in height from five to ten storeys and clustered around a sizeable communal open space. Each with its own large balcony, the spacious apartments have been arranged to ensure maximum daylight penetration: Dalston Lane now stands as an exemplar of high quality, high density housing that, through the extensive use of solid timber in its construction, offers occupants a natural and healthy living environment.

In many ways the five tall timber structures already highlighted here have been instrumental in creating an avenue in the UK for other multi-storey solid wood housing projects which, whilst not especially high by comparison, nevertheless illustrate the opportunities now available to the mainstream housebuilding sector to alter its direction of travel from traditional construction approaches that not only can be seen to be increasingly expensive and inefficient, but which fail to deliver housing in the numbers, or at the speed, required to meet demand across the UK. One such development is the slender, six-storey speculative housing block in Stoke Newington's **Barrett's Grove** (2016), by Groupwork (formerly Amin Taha Architects). Located within 20 minutes walking distance of Dalston Lane, and still within the London Borough of Hackney, the building forms a striking, well-proportioned transition in the street elevation from a five storey, Edwardian apartment block to a three-storey London County Council school.

Outwardly this appears to be a building formed from crisp, red brickwork to match in with its neighbours but closer inspection reveals the outer skin to be a rainscreen made up of double-stacked bricks with open bonds between, an architectural device that not only provides surface texture but which also makes clear that the building envelope is not loadbearing. Viewed from further along the street, the roof can also be seen to be constructed in this way, giving the impression that the block has been carved out of one material, rather than formed from an assemblage of floors topped with a conventional pitched and tiled cap. Oversized, deeply-set windows with protruding steel box frames exaggerate the building's slenderness and, to complement the organic qualities of the external surface, the enclosures to the four steel balconies that cantilever from the front elevation are wicker baskets, a decidedly un-urban, but attractive, solution formed from woven willow.

Once inside, however the story very visibly changes: this is a CLT building from bottom to top and one in which the walls, floors and inside surface of the roof have been left entirely exposed, just as the construction joints and panel edges are devoid of any covering designed to conceal the process of assembly. A clear flame-retardant coating has been applied to all of the exposed CLT surfaces, thus eschewing the need for plasterboard walls, suspended ceilings, cornices, skirting and other finishes and resulting in a substantial construction cost/time saving and a measurable reduction in the project's embodied carbon. The required acoustic build-up is provided by suspended floors into which the building's electrical and heating service runs have also been integrated, creating savings of around 15% in the overall construction cost.

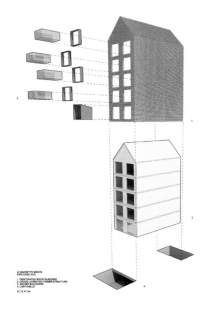

**Barrett's Grove,
London Borough of Hackney**
(2016)

Groupwork
(formerly Amin Taha Architects)
Photographer: Tim Soar

**Barrett's Grove,
London Borough of Hackney**
(2016)

Groupwork
(formerly Amin Taha Architects)
Photographer: Tim Soar

The CLT building sits over a concrete basement which contains the lower level of a three bedroom apartment (entered from the ground floor) plus front and back sunken courtyards that admit light to the living area and two of the bedrooms. The rear of the ground floor contains a single one-bedroom flat, whilst the three floors above this level each contain a two bedroom apartment. The fourth floor forms the lower level of a three bedroom apartment, the third of which, along with a study, is housed on a mezzanine set within the roof space and accessed via a final staircase internal to the flat. The common staircase, once accessed from the ground floor, is set within a CLT core from first floor to fourth floor which, whilst fair-faced, still meets fire requirements through being completely separated from the apartments and by having its exposed surfaces treated with the same clear flame retardant as used throughout the building.

In many ways this medium-rise timber building not only encapsulates many of the positive benefits inherent in CLT construction but also highlights a range of clever solutions to the delivery of high quality affordable housing in the UK. Here, nothing is disguised: the substructure, structural envelope, routes for mechanical & electrical services, finishes and landscape are effectively one and the same. In this 'what you see is what you get and what you pay for' approach the architects have circumvented conventional elemental cost packaging by themselves identifying and securing guaranteed prices from the necessary suppliers and subcontractors. The relatively straightforward technology involved in CLT construction is such that the designers of this project have—perhaps inadvertently—found themselves fulfilling the long-forgotten architect's role in which the lead professional took responsibility for the coordination of structure, services and costs and was thus able to build to budget whilst maintaining all of the design details that can give a building its special qualities. Not perhaps a model for larger and more complex projects, but one that can easily be seen to have relevance to the vast number of small to medium sites around the country that are of marginal interest to the volume housebuilding sector.

In this respect, the development at Barrett's Grove is very much an exemplar project: the architects have been able to produce a quality apartment block at a cost level affordable to housing associations and which, in this case, exceeded the developer's financial expectations by around 25%: no mean feat in London's febrile construction world. Despite the property agent's initial scepticism about exposed internal timber (which could in any case be plastered, painted or whitewashed if desired), the architects have been able to highlight the fact that the first three flats sold immediately after initial viewings, leading the agent to increase the prices for the others.

It should not be thought from the projects examined in this chapter that the only tall (or not-quite-so-tall) timber residential buildings in the UK are to be found in the London Borough of Hackney: there now exists a sufficient number of CLT residential projects scattered throughout the capital for the efficacy of this engineered timber product to be well-proven. It is the variety of approaches to be found in what is a relatively small area, however, and also the positive response to projects to date from the Borough's council, that arguably make this part of the city the world centre of excellence for the design of tall CLT residential buildings. Ever taller timber structures will continue to emerge in other cities around the globe but, at this point in time, the research and development momentum necessary to push these ambitions and desires forward and to confront the challenges presented by this evolving area of building physics unquestionably sits in London. The energy driving this use of CLT is also spilling out to other parts of the country as architects and other construction professionals throughout the UK seek new and more effective ways to respond to the massive housing supply challenge that exists today. Given the rapid expansion of projects so far, it may not be too long before we regard this form of construction as the norm rather than the exception for the development of new housing in the denser parts of our urban environments.

Chapter 13
The Timber Passivhaus

Debates about energy generation and supply, whether from nuclear, fossil fuels or renewables, and the vexed issue of government subsidies or not—and for which options—have long been current and will no doubt continue at government level well into the future. Within what might be seen as a policy vacuum, the reasons for more and more power being required and whether simply producing greater amounts of it is the most sensible energy strategy to pursue seem almost to have been forgotten. Yet it is a well-documented fact that our built environment is one of the largest consumers of energy and is extraordinarily wasteful in its use of heat and electrical power. In part, this can be attributed to the very large proportion of the country's building stock constructed before the environmental and financial cost of producing energy made us aware of the need for high levels of thermal insulation and the massive amount of alterations and improvements required to reduce heat loss through the floors, walls and roofs of the UK's existing buildings. As a consequence, whilst legislation intended to improve the quality of new homes has continued to enter the statutes over the past 30 years—which has undoubtedly introduced a degree of change in the way we design and construct housing—a culture shift is required to move beyond what often appears as grudging acceptance of regulatory change by the construction industry.

The UK property market, for example, continues in the main to preference the upfront capital expense of construction over the life cycle cost of a building (its construction, maintenance, energy use and, ultimately, deconstruction). Over an extended period of time, this has undoubtedly contributed to a lack of concern for longer-term running costs, with responsibility for these being passed on to the purchaser. *Caveat emptor* (let the buyer beware) has long been the mantra in this world, but the introduction of various consumer protection measures has led more enlightened housing developers to address the issue of wasted energy and the concomitant additional (and ever-rising) cost for home owners. In doing so, they have also begun to recognise the commercial advantages to be gained in offering highly energy-efficient buildings to the market. It is in this context that the distinctive and, more importantly, measurable, 'PassivHaus' brand has emerged as a leading standard-setter in the UK.

The concept of the Passivhaus—a home that, due to its energy-efficient construction, needs minimal or zero energy for both heating and powering electrical appliances/lighting and which is comfortable to live in through all four seasons of the year—may seem to have been around for a very long time, but was in fact first developed in Germany as recently as 1988. In the almost three decades since, the principles established for Passivhaus design and construction have been applied in widely varying climatic conditions to more than 65,000 buildings worldwide. Now well established as a global movement, and with a legitimate claim to be one of the leading international promoters of low-energy design standards, the methodology involved is monitored in the UK by the Passivhaus Trust, an independent, non-profit organisation, with

**Dundon Passivhaus,
Compton Dundon,
Somerset** (2015)
Prewett Bizley Architects
Photographer: Graham Bizley

Dursley Treehouse
Dursley, Gloucestershire (2015)
Millar Howard Workshop Ltd
Photographer: Tomás Millar

those members who have been trained and tested in the application of its standards able to become registered Passivhaus Certifiers.

So, what makes a Passivhaus different from other homes that claim to have 'low' or 'zero' carbon emissions, are highly efficient in their consumption of energy and which provide high standards of comfort and building health? The simple answer is that the Passivhaus approach comes with a well-established set of principles and standards that demand serious rigour in the building's design and construction as well as meticulous attention to detail. It is increasingly regarded as the 'gold standard' to aim for in reducing the energy requirements of new buildings, particularly new houses. Generally speaking, buildings constructed to meet its certification targets achieve at least a 75% reduction in space heating requirements compared to UK standard practice for new-build.

Essentially, there are eight standards (see box) that, in conventional housebuilding terms, may appear expensive to deliver but can, over the life of the building, demonstrate significant savings in maintenance and energy costs to substantially offset any increased capital expenditure incurred at the outset.

Passivhaus Standards
Total energy for space heating and cooling of less than 15 kWh per sq/m per year for treated floor areas
Total primary energy use for all appliances, hot water, space heating and cooling of less than 120kWh per sq/m per year (low energy household appliances are a must)
The exterior shell of the building must be insulated to a U-value not exceeding 0.15W per sq/m K
Construction must be free of thermal bridges
Houses to have a southerly orientation for solar gain
Windows with U-values not exceeding 0.8W per sq/m K for glazing and frames
At least 50% solar heat gain co-efficient through glazing
An air change rate of no more than 0.6 air changes per hour @ 50Pa

The fundamental principle of Passivhaus is simple: to reduce the heat losses of a building to such an extent that it hardly needs any heating at all. According to the Passivhaus Trust, the sun, human occupants, household appliances and the warmth from extracted air cover a large part of a house's heating demand. Passivhaus construction requirements include enhanced levels of insulation with minimal thermal bridges and well-considered use of solar and internal heat gains. As these houses are effectively airtight, whole house mechanical ventilation and heat recovery (MHVR) systems are necessary to provide highly efficient heat recovery and excellent internal air quality. Any shortfall in heating is usually met by a small unit, such as a wood-burning stove.

What does this approach have to do with timber? Meeting Passivhaus standards does not presume the use of timber construction, but arguably there are significant benefits to be had from choosing to use some form or combination of timber systems and/or technologies in the pursuit of Passivhaus excellence. Modern Methods of Construction (MMC) that make use of offsite manufacturing techniques and/or solid wood systems can, for example, ensure minimal heat loss through the consistent delivery of highly airtight construction, an attribute significantly harder to deliver using traditional masonry solutions. The consistency of these timber technologies is achieved through the fine tolerances possible with precision, factory-based manufacturing processes that are sufficiently adaptable nowadays to obviate any need for repetitive designs or serially-produced construction processes/systems. This manufacturing flexibility means the individual layout and look of a house—and the decisions about the particular construction technologies employed—remain in the hands of its owners and architects and are often dictated by site conditions.

An unusual example of this is the **Dursley Treehouse** (2015), designed by Stroud-based architects, the Millar Howard Workshop and situated in the Gloucestershire market town of Dursley. With more than 25 protected trees on the heavily wooded site, an additional planning condition was that their roots should not be affected by any new construction. The position of the trees' branches and their future growth also required careful thought, creating difficult architecture and landscape issues and made even more challenging by the desire to adhere to Passivhaus principles in the conception of the house. The design response is both practical and imaginative: practical in its use of screw pile foundations to ensure that disturbance to the ground and tree roots would be minimised; and also in these piles being used to provide the base for a steel frame that in turn supports a double-stud timber frame structure, an arrangement that allows the house to weave itself upwards through the trees. Passivhaus requirements have been met with an equally pragmatic approach: the construction method employed delivers high levels of airtightness and thermal insulation, with windows and doors located to maximise views out whilst also balancing heat losses and gains through the glazing. Heat losses have also been minimised by careful manipulation of the ratio of external surface area to volume in the house's form.

Dursley Treehouse
Dursley, Gloucestershire (2015)
Millar Howard Workshop Ltd
Photographer: Tomas Millar

It is, however, in the orchestration of the individual levels of the house that the architects have demonstrated real imagination. The building's lower floor is clad with polished stainless steel sheets to reflect the landscape within which the house sits, but this level is smaller in plan than the floors above and is thus effectively recessed and deferential to the larger, cantilevered and offset upper storeys which are clad with untreated vertical larch boards. The offset allows the middle level to double in function as an entrance and as a lightweight verandah reached by a bridge formed from galvanised metal grilles. The overall effect is of a predominantly timber house visibly distinct from the trees that surround it yet almost completely hidden amongst them and which, in its form, material and texture, entirely captures the spirit of the place. The

**The Hayshed Farmhouse,
East Ayrshire, Scotland** (2013)
Kirsty Maguire Architect Ltd
Photographer: Kirsty Maguire

complex section and hybrid construction of the Dursley treehouse demonstrates very clearly the symbiotic relationship that can exist between the attainment of Passivhaus standards and inspiring, timber-based architectural solutions.

Some 350 miles to the north, a very different architectural approach—and an alternative type of timber frame solution—is to be found in the **Hayshed Farmhouse** (2013) set on a hillside in East Ayrshire and with a distant view of the county's wet and windy western coastline. In this instance, the house, designed by Kirsty Maguire Architect Ltd, was conceived to complement the existing farm cluster and thereby root it to its agricultural context. In electing to exceed Passivhaus standards for airtightness and insulation, the architect set out to improve and refine the long-established Scottish tradition of timber frame construction. The results are impressive: the structure combines conventional platform timber frame with vertical I-joists to give the additional depth necessary to accommodate increased levels of thermal insulation, with glulam (glued laminated timber) beams used to create the roof's distinctive curved agricultural barn form. The whole building is clad with recyclable zinc sheeting coloured to match the local red earth.

With U-values for the floor, walls, roof and windows of 0.12, 0.11, 0.11 and 0.84W per sq/m K respectively, a primary energy demand of 101 kWh per sq/m per year, a space heating load of 13kWh per sq/m, an air-to-air heat pump for hot water and an air change rate of 0.22 air changes @ 50 Pa, the overall achievement is considerable, especially as there are plans to add a domestic turbine to harness the local wind and enable the house to be powered entirely from the site itself. The total floor area of 162.5 sq/m was delivered at a construction cost of £1,750 per sq/m (including internal fit out, garage and landscaping) and, as such, the house was certainly not over-expensive when it was completed in early 2014. It is the building's energy performance, however, that makes it remarkable: better than originally modelled, the energy bills are over 90% less than those of the old farmhouse. The ultimate aim is for the building to generate significantly more energy than it uses, which will provide it with the doubly-enhanced status of being a 'PlusEnergy' and 'zero carbon' house.

Another Passivhaus that reinterprets elements of rural vernacular architecture is to be found 230 miles further north. **Tigh na Croit** (2014) stands at Gorstan, near Garve in Ross-shire and is one of the most northerly projects in the UK to have gained certified Passivhaus status. Situated in an area of former crofting land, it is no surprise that its design, by the Glasgow office of HLM Architects, takes inspiration for its form and scale from the traditional Highland steading (a small farm and its buildings). As with the Haystead Farmhouse, the new 3-bed dwelling—aside from some grey-stained panels of vertical cladding—conceals its more serious timber credentials beneath its exterior: the traditional outer skin of white render on blockwork conceals a heavily insulated, 300mm deep, prefabricated twin-stud timber frame. The architects had previously used this system in a small, timber-clad Passivhaus terrace it had designed for Scotland's Housing Expo, a cluster of 55 experimental house designs built in 2010 at Milton of Leys near Inverness. The clients for Tigh na Croit, well aware of the need for high levels of airtightness and thermal insulation in the house's exposed northerly location, were keen to replicate this proven approach in their new home.

They also wished to acknowledge the L-shaped plan form of typical local farm dwellings, a technical challenge for the architects since most Passivhaus projects tend to have square or rectangular footprints in order to minimise external surface area and to allow the whole building to be oriented towards the south. In response, the house has been planned as two wings with the longer of these designed to ensure the main living spaces face south and thereby make the most of solar gains whilst the bedroom wing looks to the east to benefit from morning sunlight. Given its rural location and the difficulty of finding contractors (never mind any that might have experience of Passivhaus construction) to work in remote areas, the house's overall floor area of 223.5 per sq/m and cost of £1614 per sq/m on completion in June 2014 can be seen as

**Tigh na Croit,
Gorstan, near Garve,
Ross-shire,
Scottish Highlands** (2014)
HLM Architects
Photographer: Keith Hunter

**Dundon Passivhaus,
Compton Dundon,
Somerset** (2015)

Prewett Bizley Architects
Photographer: Graham Bizley

extremely good value, especially with its primary energy demand of only 97 kW per sq/m per year, space heating load of 13 kWh per sq/m and an air change rate of 0.6 air changes @ 50 Pa. U-Values too, delivered via the super-insulated building fabric, are well within Passivhaus standards at 0.107, 0.114, 0.109 and 0.755W per sq/m K for floors, walls, roof and windows respectively, resulting in an 80% reduction in energy consumption.

The Passivhaus approach, whilst obviously well-suited to the more extreme climatic conditions that often prevail north of the border, is equally applicable to projects in rural parts of England. The **Dundon Passivhaus** (2015) sits at the foot of a wooded hill overlooking the Somerset levels, an area of the country that came to wide public attention when it suffered extensive and long-lasting flooding in the severe winter of 2013-14. Located five miles south of Glastonbury in the village of Compton Dundon and designed by the local office of Prewett Bizley Architects, the house replaced a dilapidated 1920s bungalow. Uniquely, it embraces several of the characteristics highlighted in other chapters of this book: it is not only Passivhaus certified, it is also rural with green timber structural elements and cladding, has a softwood timber frame and was self-built by the architect-owner for his family. The latter point may explain why this house ticks so many boxes relevant to the content of this book: the architect's aim from the outset—apart from a desire to use the minimum amount of energy—was to explore the extent to which the possibilities of a certified Passivhaus might be pushed. One outcome of this has been the use of locally-sourced renewable materials in maintaining a harmonious relationship between the house and the landscape it sits within.

The four-bedroom house has, therefore, been dug into the hillside, a stratagem that ensured the overall height of the two-storey house would barely exceed that of the bungalow previously on the site, an important factor in planning permission being granted for the new dwelling. The rear of the lower floor contains a row of service rooms such as bathroom, plant, storage and utility that have no special requirement for natural light and which, together, effectively form an additional passive thermal barrier—a 'thick wall'—between the house's interior and the cold ground it butts up against.

In its visible form, the house is very definitely designed to follow function: thick, heavily insulated timber-framed walls are vertically clad with rough-sawn green oak boards, while an outrigger green oak post and beam structure, tied back to the timber frame, supports the shallow pitched roof planes. These extend beyond the footprint of the house to offer shade and shelter to ground floor terraces as well as a wraparound first floor verandah that faces to both east and west to catch the sun throughout the day. The house's range of internal timber finishes are exposed—the upper floor entrance hall and reception rooms are lined in planed oak with oak joinery, with other areas lined with plywood painted in warm shades of grey. This, simple approach, in combination with the house's vapour permeable wall construction, allows the hygroscopic nature of the wood to contribute positively to the air quality within the internal spaces. For its size (226 sq/m) and with a measured primary energy demand of 85kWh per sq/m per year, the Dundon Passivhaus is unquestionably a very low energy building. It is also a quintessential demonstration of the contribution timber construction can make to ensuring a house can deliver to Passivhaus standards.

Some 90 or so miles away at Chieveley, near Newbury and in the North Wessex Downs area of outstanding natural beauty (AONB) stands the **Old Water Tower** (2015), a new four-bedroom house designed by Gresford Architects to show that the Passivhaus philosophy not only produces highly sustainable buildings, but that these can also be crisply-detailed examples of good modern architecture. Importantly, it has also been developed by the architects as a commercial proposition to demonstrate that a certified Passivhaus such as this need not be more expensive to build than comparably-sized dwellings using other forms of construction. Like Tigh na Croit and the Hayshed Farmhouse, the Old Water Tower is a contemporary interpretation of vernacular farm structures. In this instance, local historic timber frame buildings have provided the precedent and, from a distance, the house visibly evokes the form, scale and simplicity of a traditional agricultural shed.

The main structure of the house is a prefabricated, 300mm deep, twin-stud timber frame filled with blown cellulose insulation and procured from a company that specialises in the manufacture of this type of timber system for Passivhaus projects. Unusually too, the timber cladding is a branded product from France that makes excellent use of Douglas fir, a softwood classified as a moderately durable species but which, with appropriate preservative treatment, is extensively specified in that country for external use. It is less commonly used for this purpose in the UK since, in the generally preferred untreated form, its lifespan falls within the 10-15 year bracket. This is likely to be extended in this case by the grey pre-coating it received in the manufacturer's factory.

Unlike most Passivhaus designs, the Old Water Tower is oriented to the west, with large windows to take advantage of the views over open countryside—an important selling point for a commercial development. The southern elevation has large windows at ground floor level whilst the first floor above has small, randomly-positioned windows set high in the wall, drawing comparisons with traditional dovecot openings. With external blinds on the east, south and west elevations that operate automatically when internal temperatures reach 21 degrees and with triple-glazed openable windows, this is a technically-sophisticated project aimed at a specific sector of the housing market. As such, its visible and elegant use of timber demonstrates the extent to which home-owner perceptions of the material have changed and that it is no longer regarded as a cheap and impermanent option. In this instance, and with a build time of only six months, the 200 sq/m house had a construction cost of £1,750 per sq/m when completed in October 2015: a relatively inexpensive outcome, given the quality and outstanding energy performance achieved.

The Passivhaus approach is not only suitable for detached houses in rural situations: timber-based Passivhaus projects are increasingly to be found in high-density urban areas. One of the first UK examples of such is to be found in the London Borough of Camden. Completed in Spring 2010 and designed by Bere Architects, the 118 sq/m, two-bed **Ranulf Road Passivhaus** (2010) was the first Certified Passivhaus to be built in the capital, a significant achievement at the time. The architects had in fact already developed a highly energy-conscious design for the client who—wishing to achieve a comfortable, healthy home that had minimum energy consumption—made the decision to aim for Passivhaus standards. Thereafter—and with the use of the Passivhaus Planning Package (PHPP—readily-available software for designers), that helps determine the optimum site position for a house, as well as the optimum orientation and percentage of its glazing—the design development process went through many iterations before arriving at the final, implemented solution.

The site in question was small and tight, both features that gave some cause for concern to the local planning authority as regards the positioning of the house. The PHPP studies, however, made clear the need for a compact, freestanding house with south-facing glazing and for a more efficient relationship between its floor area and the rest of the building envelope. The house plan was thus moved to the north of the site, a change that freed up land for a south facing garden and an upper terrace. This strategic shift created the opportunity for bright, naturally lit internal spaces whilst also reducing the visual impact of the house when seen from the street, a point that had been a particular issue for the local planners. As an indication that Passivhaus standards require many challenges to be addressed before a final robust solution is arrived at, ten more design variations for this small house were explored in detail. The end result confirms the value of this rigorous process: as constructed, the house has well-lit, airy rooms with large, south-facing triple-glazed sliding windows. As an early precursor to projects like the Old Water Tower, it also has external, automatically-controlled blinds on its south elevation to control summer temperatures, with high levels of insulation to its two green roofs (both of which are of prefabricated solid timber construction). Externally, the house is clad with horizontal, open-jointed and untreated Siberian larch slats.

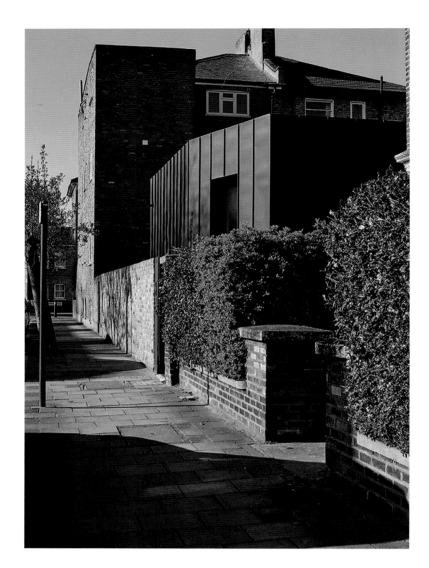

Lansdowne Drive,
London Borough of Hackney
(2015)
Tectonics Architects
Photographer: Bernard Tulkens

Urban sites for individual houses are increasingly hard to come by nowadays, are invariably expensive and often have less than ideal design constraints due to their position in relation to adjacent existing buildings. Add to these issues the extra complications of Passivhaus design and the architectural challenges increase immeasurably. An example that combines practically all of these factors, with the added curveball of being in a Conservation Area in the East London Borough of Hackney, is the partly-sunk, two-storey house at **Lansdowne Drive** (2015) designed by Tectonics Architects. Sitting immediately adjacent to a four-storey Victorian terrace which prevents direct sun reaching the former garden site from the south, the usual Passivhaus criteria regarding orientation and advantageous use of solar gain have had to be eschewed and new solutions found in order to achieve the overall standards required. The design, therefore, involves a hybrid approach in which the half-sunken lower level is formed from poured in-situ reinforced concrete, with the upper walls, intermediate floor and roof constructed with prefabricated cross laminated timber (CLT) panels. The many benefits of the latter are discussed elsewhere in this book: suffice to say that once delivered to site, the panels forming this house were erected without problem within a mere two days. Notably too, wood fibre insulation was fixed to the panel exteriors, a key innovation of the project, allowing the internal wall surfaces to remain fair-faced and thus making a positive contribution to the internal air quality of the rooms. In line with this visible construction aesthetic, all other elements such as the structural concrete, electrical conduits and MVHR ducts, have also been left exposed. In sharp contrast, the outer skin of the building is formed from tailored, grey standing-seam zinc sheeting.

Internally, the house has its bedrooms and bathrooms situated at lower level, allowing the upper, ground floor to be completely open plan which, free of any intervening supporting structure, allows the kitchen and dining zone to the south end of the room to flow into the daylight-filled living space.

This 94 sq/m house is undoubtedly compact and almost completely fills its site, except for a very small external area on its west-facing lower level. Nevertheless—and notwithstanding the design constraints highlighted earlier—its clever design manages to deliver a primary energy demand figure of 83.73 kWh per sq/m per year, a heating demand of 13.64 kWh per sq/m and an airtightness factor of 0.29 air changes @ 50 Pa. The highly-insulated building envelope has U-values of 0.103, 0.113, 0.074 and 0.06W per sq/m K for the house's floor, walls, roof and windows respectively: a significant achievement that once again demonstrates the merits of solid timber construction.

Ever-rising costs have focused public attention on how energy consumption might be reduced in the average home. As a consequence, more and more houses in the UK today are being built—and sold—with some assessment offered of their likely energy usage, but there is no doubt that evolving regulations will continue to increase the demand for higher levels of insulation and draught-free construction. This, together with rising house prices, is likely to bring energy costs into ever-sharper focus, with designs needing to clearly demonstrate their overall efficiency in this regard. Building a dwelling to Passivhaus standards has often been thought to have a cost premium attached, but the examples included here can ably demonstrate this need not be the case. As the number of Passivhaus projects continues to increase in the UK, so too will the range of experience attained by the architects and engineers involved and, with this, the likely emergence of greater design and construction efficiencies. Passivhaus is not the only energy-efficient design game in town, but its clear branding and high, measurable standards currently set it apart from other approaches. Increased public awareness may even bring demand for all new homes to achieve certified Passivhaus status. At present, only 1% of the UK's 33,000+ registered architects can also claim to be Certified Passivhaus Designers, but a considerably higher percentage aspire to design to Passivhaus standards. Many of those who do so are also finding the simplest delivery route lies in the use of modern timber technologies.

Chapter 14

The Future Timber House

Predicting the future is well understood to be a fool's game. Nevertheless, there are many issues in housing that refuse to go away and for which solutions remain to be found. Some, like the changes to land ownership and available financial mechanisms that are arguably necessary to increase the supply and quality of new housing are beyond the scope of this book, but others relate to the way we use land, the places where we choose to build, the ways we build and the cultural, economic and environmental impact of what we build.

An important land-related issue that has manifested itself in recent years to catastrophic effect has been the dramatic increase in the number of houses constructed on flood plains. The logic of doing so has been simple: land categorised for this purpose has previously had a low value attached to it since it was unsuited for building upon but, if purchased at this reduced price and a subsequent planning permission acquired for new houses, its value might be raised significantly and any houses built upon it sold at a considerable premium to their actual land and construction cost. Unfortunately, such houses as have been built have largely followed traditional developer models and have taken little or no cognisance, in their design or construction, of an area's potential to flood. Long periods with no flood activity perhaps encouraged complacency and, with pressure on local authorities to encourage more house building within their jurisdiction, an arguably more lenient view of planning applications has resulted in many flood plains around the country being built upon: figures for 2001-2014 indicate around 200,000 homes were constructed during that period in flood zones around the UK. The major floods of recent winters that caused extensive damage to homes and communities have, however, thrown into stark relief the economic and social consequences of a collective failure to recognise or remember why certain areas of land have traditionally been left as passive defences against the ability of rivers and sea to rise dramatically in level.

This radical change in land use has divided views on how the problem should be addressed: on the one hand, it has brought about many calls for a blanket ban to be implemented on building in flood-prone areas. Others have argued that it is possible to build more intelligently on floodplains, but that no construction should be allowed until genuinely intelligent—and necessarily innovative—solutions are developed and rigorously tested. The exceptional weather that caused floods to cover much of the Somerset Levels in south-west England in the winter of 2013-14 demonstrated that, when these problems arise, the area of land to suddenly disappear under water can be enormous: the Environment Agency estimated that during that period more than 65 million cubic metres of floodwater covered an area of 65 square kilometres. There is no single reason why such extensive flooding arises: failure to dredge rivers or to maintain existing flood barriers being just two examples highlighted during the emergency in Somerset, but new flood defence strategies will require large-scale planning, holistic system design and a great deal of time and money.

Water Lane,
Oxfordshire (2015)
Baca Homes
Photographer: Alastair Lever

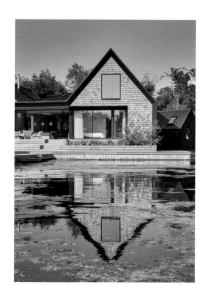

Backwater (2016)
Platform 5 Architects
Photographer: Alan Williams

Meanwhile, some individual examples of non-standard approaches to the design of high quality, flood-resilient homes have been constructed in areas prone to fluctuating water levels and offer interesting pointers as to how mass housing solutions might be developed in the future—especially for flood plain locations that have, in recent years, been subject not only to a significant expansion in building construction, but where climate change may introduce widespread and long-lasting inundation and become a more regular occurrence. Even where flooding can, on past evidence, be presumed, the attractions of the location may, for some people, triumph over the inherent construction challenges. Nevertheless, the technical issues require solutions and often considerable innovation to deliver homes that are not only secure, but also insurable.

A place with a long history of flooding is the Norfolk Broads, so much so that historical recorded measurements of the rise in water levels provide valuable information for the design of foundations and the necessary elevation of a building's lowest floors. A good example of this, The Haven at Horning, featured earlier in this book (Chapter 4—The Modified Timber House). Also on the Broads, **Backwater** (2016), near Wroxham, by Platform 5 Architects, is similarly raised on piles which, in this instance, required to be driven down a full 10 metres into the chalk rock layer. A grillage of galvanised steel ground beams were mounted on these in order to elevate the house sufficiently to accommodate changing water levels. This limited use of concrete, and the reduction in time on site required to form the substructure, allowed the early construction of a dry deck upon which the house's stick-built timber frame superstructure could be erected.

The latter combination of engineered and traditional timber components was selected for the very practical reason that, being located on a secluded promontory, transportation of materials to the site was limited to a narrow access road, with other elements delivered by boat. Cross laminated timber and panelised systems were discounted because there was no crane access. Most of the timber specified was standard softwood structural material and easily available on short lead times, with additional justification for the use of timber frame construction being its high strength-to-weight ratio, its workability on site and the ease and speed of its assembly. Use of timber also minimised the load on the substructure and was adaptable to complex, bespoke connections within the roofs.

Water Lane,
Oxfordshire (2015)
Baca Homes
Photographer/CGI: Alastair Lever

The lightweight pitched roofs of Backwater's three low-rise, splayed bays are, therefore, supported on a regular arrangement of timber portal frames, allowing the spaces below to stand as spacious, vaulted volumes. The highly insulated building shell was designed to deliver exceptional levels of airtightness, with an MHVR system provided to minimise heat loss through ventilation. Again, the lightweight timber construction provided a positive benefit, due to quicker warm-up times that reduce the need for prolonged use of heating systems and their consequent running costs.

The preference for timber construction is also evident on Backwater's exterior. The side walls and roofs are clad with blackened western red cedar shingles in order to better express the dwelling's form as an abstracted, folded plane. The front and rear elevations are also shingled, but have been left untreated to allow them to weather naturally and develop a warm, textured appearance. Layered timber decking projects from the house's waterside frontage to provide external space that is usable throughout the seasons and to act as a transition from water level up to the elevated ground floor.

Beyond its role as a sustainable family home, Backwater demonstrates the viability of building on a flood plain, providing simple principles are observed. Elevating the building on piles is not especially innovative, but it is a practical and a well-proven solution that works. As such, it is an object lesson to developers thinking of building on sites liable to flooding, as is the common-sense use of lightweight timber structures on top.

Across in Oxfordshire, the name of the next house perhaps gives an indication of its location's propensity to flood. Set in a historic village so old that it is recorded in the Doomsday Book. **Water Lane** (2015), designed by floating architecture specialists, Baca Architects, is an elevated family home that stands in a leafy garden. The site has a brook running along its edge and, during periods of high rainfall, the water level can rise sufficiently to flood the garden. The need to raise the house above the highest recorded flood point has, therefore, been approached very differently here, with a solution in which the surrounding landscape has been sculpted to accept encroaching water and provide a gradual warning of its advance. Additional swales, permeable paving and other sustainable drainage measures (SuDS) all contribute to an environmental strategy designed to reduce the run-off into the stream and thereby lessen the risk of the brook overflowing its banks.

The architectural approach taken complements this landscape solution by raising the house above its piled foundations on wooden blocks that support an elevated deck. This scheme allows water to flow freely under the house, rather than let it continue to rise and enter the ground floor, a concept that, during dry spells, has resulted in the impression of the dwelling appearing to levitate. A heavily insulated, timber frame superstructure has been used to form four inter-locking volumes, broken down in mass, to define the house's different functions—living, dining, cooking and sleeping—and to complement the scale of other buildings in the village. The rooms are all interconnected but vary in ceiling height and volume. Water Lane's plan is arranged around an open deck area that separates the living accommodation from the bedroom wing. The house's exterior has a rainscreen cladding formed from horizontally-fixed larch slats, some of which, in front of the tops of windows, are routed to maximise light into the interiors whilst also providing solar shading.

As with Backwater, the flood-resilience strategy evolved for Water Lane has been founded upon sustainability principles which here extend to including the treatment of the surrounding landscape to provide a passive means of distributing the waters in the least-damaging way: not only to the house itself, but also to trees and neighbouring properties. It is a solution that, on appropriate sites, has potential for enlargement to multiple house developments.

The final house to be explored for its capacity to counter the worst effects of flooding takes an altogether more radical approach, not only in its design, but also in its use of materials. **Redshank** (2016), by Lisa Shell Architects, is to be found at Lee-Over-Sands in Essex, a remote hamlet community of 34 homes located between Mersea Island and Clacton-on-Sea which was, pre-war, a holiday resort of sorts. This is a flat, alien landscape that embraces everything from wind farms to caravan parks. The dwellings on Beach Road stand along one side of what is really a rough track: Redshank stands on the other. The house was built as a retreat for an artist-couple and the influence of their input to its design is evident in its unusual sculptural form. The starting points for the architect, however, were a concern for the preservation of the local natural environment and the need to raise the building high enough above the area's propensity to flood—in January 2017, the threat of severe coastal flooding led to a plan to evacuate over 2500 homes in Lee-Over-Sands and nearby Jaywick. In the event, the plan was never implemented, but a recent bad flood in the area produced more than one metre of water.

**Redshank,
Lee-Over-Sands, Essex** (2016)
Lisa Shell Architects
Photographer: Hélène Binet

Redshank is raised on three elliptical steel legs (painted red, hence the name) that are 2.4 metres high and sit on a concrete raft foundation. The steel framework had to be substantial enough to support the small house's cross laminated timber superstructure but would have been even more robust had it been required to hold up a heavier material. The choice of this product was also dictated by its very low embodied carbon footprint and its capacity to form the house's floor, walls and roof. Redshank's internal surfaces have been left unfinished, the warmth of the wood adding to the ambience of the house. In this particular instance, the design has moved the CLT manufacturing process beyond the delivery of a simple panel solution into one that has taken full sculptural advantage of the product's outstanding properties (as highlighted in Chapter 3—The Solid Timber House).

It is the exterior of Redshank, however, that takes the house somewhere into the future in terms of material development. The CLT has been clad with ridged, agglomerated cork panels that are dimensionally-stable, fireproof and insulating. A by-product of cork manufacture for bottles, the bark is hand-stripped from ancient Portuguese cork oaks, which renew themselves to produce future harvests. The agglomeration process involves pressure and heat only, without any chemical additives and therefore produces a non-hazardous and biodegradable product. Importantly, as regards Redshank's location, it is also highly resistant to damp, mould and infestation. The option to give the cork a polyurethane coating was rejected, the preference here being to let the material respond to the vagaries of the weather and the local atmospheric conditions. The CLT box is entirely covered with cork and, since rain simply drains off its surfaces, there is no need for gutters to interrupt the building's sculptural simplicity. This is a material from another more primitive time but, in this landscape, it seems not only entirely appropriate and may well open the door to new thinking about how time-honoured materials might be used in entirely new and passive ways.

To return to where this book began and to Martin Heidegger's proposition that when building becomes associated with the mere construction of houses, it becomes habitual and, as a consequence, we tend to forget what we mean by building (as dwelling). As a possible solution to the UK's housing crisis, Redshank is unlikely be to everyone's taste but, as the progenitor of other innovative possibilities, this small studio may well signal an entirely different future for the way we build houses and the qualities we require from them to ensure we have homes in which we have made a positive choice to dwell. This book has put forward a case for timber, in all its forms, to be considered essential to the next generation of houses in the UK and it is hoped the examples included will provide the inspiration for architects and others to push forward the boundaries for the use of this wonderful, natural and renewable resource.

Featured Buildings and Credits

Part One
Modern Timber Technologies

Living Wall, Bury St. Edmunds (2008)
Studio MGM / Modece
www.molearchitects.co.uk
Photographer: Matthew Smith

Chapter 01
The Green Timber House

Twilly Springs House, West Hendred, nr. Wantage, Oxfordshire (2009-13)
Diamond Architects
www.diamondarchitects.co.uk
Photographer: David Grandorge

Newstead, Bottom Lane, Seer Green, Buckinghamshire (2010)
Baca Architects
www.baca.uk.com
Photographer: Alastair Lever

Frisealach, Roshven (2008)
Helen Lucas Architects
www.helenlucas.co.uk
Photographer: Brendan MacNeill

Taigh na Coille, Loch Ailort (2012)
Helen Lucas Architects
www.helenlucas.co.uk
Photographer: Angus Bremner

Caretaker's House, Hooke Park, Dorset (2012)
Invisible Studio with AA Intermediate Unit 2
www.invisiblestudio.org
Photographer: Valerie Bennett

Chapter 02
The Prefabricated Timber House

Stick Built Timber Frame

Woodpeckers, New Forest (2015)
Ström Architects
www.stromarchitects.com
Photographer: Luke Hayes

The Mill, Southside Steading, Scottish Borders (2014)
WT Architecture
www.wtarchitecture.com
Photographer: Andrew Lee

Ott's Yard, Tufnell Park,North London (2014)
VPPR Architects
http://vppr.co.uk
Photographer:
Tatiana von Preussen / Hélène Binet

The Crow's Nest, Lyme Regis, Dorset (2016)
AR Design Studio
www.ardesignstudio.co.uk
Photographer: Martin Gardner

North Vat, Dungeness (2014)
Rodic Davidson Architects
https://rodicdavidson.co.uk
Photographer: Hélène Binet

Timber Frame Open-Panel House

The Sett, Totland, Isle of Wight (2014)
Dow Jones Architects
http://dowjonesarchitects.com
Photographer: David Grandorge

Timber Frame Closed-Panel House

Cinque Ports Street, Rye (2015)
JD Architects
http://www.jdarchitects.co.uk
Photographer: Oliver Perrott

The Structural Insulated Panels (SIP) House

House in the Woods, South Downs National Park (2015)
alma-nac
www.alma-nac.com
Photographer: Jack Hobhouse

Howe Farm, Buckinghamshire (2016)
IPT Architects
http://iptarch.co.uk
Photographer: Andy Spain

Great House Farm, Phase One,Cardiff (2015)
Gillard Associates Architecture & Design
http://www.gillardassociates.co.uk
Photographer: Alan Gillard

Strathblane House, Strathblane, Stirlingshire (2013)
ATA Studio
www.atastudio.com
Photographer: David Barbour

Chapter 03
The Solid Timber House

Sunken House, London Borough of Hackney (2007)
Adjaye Associates
www.adjaye.com
Photographer: Ed Reeve

Carmarthen Place, Bermondsey, London (2007)
Architects in Residence (AiR)
Photographer: Riko Hise

Strange House, Deptford, South London (2010)
Hugh Strange Architects
www.hughstrange.com
Photographer: David Grandorge

WoodBlock House, London (2013)
dRMM
www.drmm.co.uk
Photographer: Alex de Rijke

Mazarin House, Woodford, East London (2014)
Arboreal Architecture
www.arborealarchitecture.com
Photographer: Tom Raymont

Dune House, Thorpeness, Suffolk (2010)
Jarmund Vigsnaes AS Arkitekter MNAL in association with Mole Architects
www.jva.no
http://www.molearchitects.co.uk
Photographer: Jarmund Vigsnaes AS Arkitekter / MNAL

Sussex House, South Downs (2014)
Wilkinson King Architects
www.wilkinsonking.com
Photographer: Paul Riddle

Downley House, South Downs National Park (2012)
Birds Portchmouth Russia
www.birdsportchmouthrussum.com
Photographer: Christopher Taee

Plummerswood, Innerleithen, Scottish Borders (2011)
Gaia Architects
www.gaiagroup.org
Photographer: Michael Wolchover

Chapter 08
The Extended Timber House

51A Gloucester Crescent,
London Borough of Camden (2010)
John Glew Architects
www.johnglew.co.uk
Photography: John Glew

Austen House,
North Walls, Winchester (2015)
Adam Knibb Architects
www.adamknibbarchitects.com
Photography: Martin Gardner

The Dairy House, Somerset (2008)
Skene Catling de la Pena
www.scdlp.net
Photography: James Morris

The Hurdle House,
Alresford, Hampshire (2016)
Adam Knibb Architects
www.adamknibbarchitects.com
Photography: James Morris

Bonnington Grove, Edinburgh (2015)
Konishi Gaffney Architects
www.konishigaffney.com
Photography: Andrew Lee

Stamford Road, Dalston,
London Borough of Hackney (2016)
Pamphilon Architects
http://www.pamphilonarchitects.com
Photographer: Anna Pamphilon

147 De Beauvoir Road, Kingsland,
London Borough of Hackney (2013)
Scott Architects
www.scottarch.co.uk
Photography: Lyndon Douglas

Black House, Fortescue Avenue,
Hackney, London (2017)
Simon Conder Architects
www.simonconder.co.uk
Photography: Paul Smoothy

Chapter 09
The Suburban Timber House

Herringbone Houses, Lyford Road,
Wandsworth, London (2007)
Alison Brooks Architects
http://www.alisonbrooksarchitects.com
Photographer: Christobal Palma

Chestnut, Newport Road,
Barnes, West London (2010)
David Long Architects
http://dlaltd.com
Photographer: David Long

Cavendish Avenue, Cambridge (2008)
Mole Architects
http://www.molearchitects.co.uk
Photographer: David Butler

Woodstock, Worsley,
West Manchester (2008)
Stephenson Studio
http://www.stephenson-studio.com
Photographer: Stephenson Studio

25-25a Hurst Avenue,
Highgate, London (2013)
Waugh Thistleton Architects
http://waughthistleton.com
Photographer: Bliss Space

The Cedar Lodges,
Winchester, Hampshire (2015)
Adam Knibb Architects
https://www.adamknibbarchitects.com
Photographer: Martin Gardner

Chapter 10
The Regional Timber House

Tigh Port na Long, Aird of Sleat,
Isle of Skye (2011)
Dualchas
https://www.dualchas.com
Photographer: Andrew Lee

Borreraig, Glendale, Isle of Skye (2011)
Dualchas
https://www.dualchas.com
Photographer: Andrew Lee

Colbost, Waternish, Isle of Skye (2012)
Dualchas
https://www.dualchas.com
Photographer: Andrew Lee

The Cliff House, Galtrigill, Isle of Skye (2014)
Dualchas
https://www.dualchas.com
Photographer: Andrew Lee

Fiskavaig, Isle of Skye (2010)
Rural Design
http://www.ruraldesign.co.uk
Photographer: Andrew Lee

Turf House, Kendram, Isle of Skye (2012)
Rural Design
http://www.ruraldesign.co.uk
Photographer: Nigel Rigden

R.HOUSE
Rural Design with James MacQueen Builders
http://www.ruralhouse.co.uk
Photographer: Nigel Rigden

Heb Homes
Dualchas
https://www.hebrideanhomes.com
Photographer: Dualchas

Camusdarrach Sands (2013)
Raw Architecture Workshop
http://www.rawarchitectureworkshop.com
Photographer: David Barbour

Chapter 11
The Hybrid Timber House

Strathdon House, Cairngorms National Park, Newe, Strathdon, Aberdeenshire (2016)
Brown + Brown Architects
http://www.brownandbrownarchitects.com
Photography: Brown + Brown Architects

Broad Street House, Orford, Suffolk (2015)
Nash Baker Architects
http://www.nashbaker.co.uk
Photography: Nick Gutteridge

The Arboretum, North Norfolk coast (2014)
Cowper Griffiths Architects
http://www.cowpergriffith.co.uk
Photographer: Peter Cook

Sweethaws, Redbridge Lane, Sweethaws Wood, East Sussex (2013)
Smerin Architects
http://www.smerin.co.uk
Photographer: Tim Crocker

Steambent House, Cornwall (2016)
Tom Raffield
www.tomraffield.com
Photographer: Kirstin Prisk

Chapter 12
The Tall Timber House

Stadthaus, Murray Grove, London Borough of Hackney (2009)
Waugh Thistleton Architects
http://waughthistleton.com
Photographer: Will Pryce

Bridport House, London Borough of Hackney (2011)
Karakusevic Carson Architects
http://karakusevic-carson.com
Photographer: Ioana Marinescu

Whitmore Road, London Borough of Hackney (2012)
Waugh Thistleton Architects
http://waughthistleton.com
Photographer: Will Pryce / Waugh Thistleton Architects

The Cube, Banyan Wharf, London (2015)
Wenlock Road, London Borough of Hackney
Hawkins\Brown Architects
https://www.hawkinsbrown.com
Photographer: Jack Hobhouse

Dalston Lane, London Borough of Hackney (2017)
Waugh Thistleton Architects
http://waughthistleton.com
Photographer: DanielShearing / Waugh Thistleton Architects

Barrett's Grove, London Borough of Hackney (2016)
Groupwork (formerly Amin Taha Architects)
http://amintaha.co.uk
Photographer: Tim Soar

Chapter 13
The Timber Passivhaus

Dursley Treehouse Dursley, Gloucestershire (2015)
Millar Howard Workshop Ltd
mhworkshop.co.uk
Photographer: Tomas Millar

The Hayshed Farmhouse, East Ayrshire, Scotland (2013)
Kirsty Maguire Architect Ltd
www.kirstymaguire.com
Photographer: Kirsty Maguire

Tigh na Croit, Gorstan, near Garve, Ross-shire, Scottish Highlands (2014)
HLM Architects
www.hlmarchitects.com
Photographer: Keith Hunter

Dundon Passivhaus, Compton Dundon, Somerset (2015)
Prewett Bizley Architects
www.prewettbizley.com
Photographer: Graham Bizley

The Old Water Tower, Chieveley, nr. Newbury, West Berkshire (2015)
Gresford Architects
www.gresfordarchitects.co.uk
Photographer: Quintin Lake

Ranulf Road Passivhaus, London Borough of Camden (2010)
Bere Architects
www.bere.co.uk
Photographer: Tim Crocker

Lansdowne Drive, London Borough of Hackney (2015)
Tectonics Architects
www.tectonics-architects.com
Photographer: Bernard Tulkens

Chapter 14
The Future Timber House

Water Lane, Oxfordshire (2015)
Baca Homes
http://bacahomes.co.uk
Photographer: Alastair Lever

Backwater (2016)
Platform 5 Architects
https://platform5architects.com
Photographer: Alan Williams

Redshank, Lee-Over-Sands, Essex (2016)
Lisa Shell Architects
http://www.lisashellarchitects.co.uk
Photographer: Hélène Binet

Bibliography

Part 1

General

Norberg-Schulz C. *The Concept of Dwelling - on the way to figurative architecture*. New York: Rizzoli International Publications Inc., 1984

Wachsmann K. - *Building the Wooden House - Technique and Design*. First published in German, 1930. Basel: Birkhäuser Verlag GmbH, 1995

Herzog T., Natterer J., Schweitzer R., Voll M., Winter W. - *Timber Construction Manual*. Basel: Birkhäuser Verlag GmbH, 2004

Kolb J. - *Systems in Timber Engineering*. Basel: Birkhäuser Verlag GmbH, 2008

Davies I., Wood J.B., *External Timber Cladding - Design, Installation and Performance*. Edinburgh: Arcamedia, 2010

Davies I. - *Sustainable Construction Timber - Sourcing and Specifying Local Timber*. Edinburgh: Forestry Commission, 2nd Edition, 2016

Farmer M. *Modernise or Die - the Farmer Review of the UK Construction Labour Model*. London: Construction Leadership Council (CLC), October 2016

Fixing our Broken Housing Market. London: Department for Communities and Local Government, February 2017

Chapter 1 - The Green Timber House

Brunskill R.W. - *Timber Building In Britain*. First published 1985. Paperback, second impression 2004

Harris R. - *Discovering Timber-Framed Buildings*. Princes Risborough: Shire Publications Ltd: first published 1978; 3rd revised edition 1993

Newman R. - *Oak-Framed Buildings*. Lewes, East Sussex: GMC Publications Ltd, 2005

Ross P., Mettem C., Holloway A - *Green Oak in Construction*. High Wycombe: TRADA, 2007

Chapter 2 - The Prefabricated Timber House

Hairstans R. - *Off-site and Modern Methods of Timber Construction - a sustainable approach*. High Wycombe: TRADA 2010

Hairstans R. - *Building Offsite - an Introduction*. Edinburgh: Arcamedia, 2016

Kapfinger O., Wieler U. - *Riess Wood 3 Modulare Holbausysteme*. Wien: Springer Verlag, 2007

Chapter 3 - The Solid Timber House

Eds. Waugh A., Weiss K-H., Wells M. - *A Process Revealed*. London: FUEL Design & Publishing, 2009

Mayo J. - *Solid Wood - Case Studies in Mass Timber Architecture, Technology and Design*. Abingdon, Oxon: Routledge, 2015

Eds. Kaufmann H., Nerdinger W. - *Building with Timber - Paths into the Future*. London: Prestel, 2011

Chapter 4 - The Modified Timber House

Hill C. - *Wood Modification: Chemical, Thermal and Other Processes*. London: Wiley, 2006

Part 2

Chapter 5 - The Affordable Timber House

Karakusevic P., Batchelor A. - *Social Housing Definitions and Design Exemplars*. London: RIBA Publishing, 2017

Chapter 7 - The Remodelled Timber House

Scott F. - *On Altering Architecture*. London & New York Routledge, 2008

Bloszies C. - *Old Buildings, New Designs : Architectural Transformations*. New York: Princeton Architectural Press, 2011

Chapter 10 - The Regional Timber House

Frampton, K. - *Towards a Critical Regionalism: Six Points for an Architecture of Resistance*. In Foster, H. (ed). *Postmodern Culture*. pp.16-30. London; Pluto Press, 1983

Lefaivre L., Tzonis A. - *Critical Regionalism - Architecture and Identity in a Globalised World*. London; Prestel Verlag, 2003

Norberg-Schulz C. - *Genius Loci: Towards a Phenomenology of Architecture*. New York, Rizzoli International Publications Inc., 1980

Maudlin D. - *The Highland House Transformed: Architecture and Identity on the Edge of Britain, 1700-1850*. Dundee; Dundee University Press, 2010

Reiach A., Hurd R. - *Building Scotland - a Cautionary Guide*. Edinburgh; Saltire Society,1944

Planning & Architecture Division *Planning Advice Note 72 - Housing in the Countryside*, Edinburgh, Scottish Government, 2005

Chapter 12 - The Tall Timber House

Green M. - *The Case for Tall Wood Buildings - How Mass Timber Offers a Safe, Economical, and Environmentally Friendly Alternative for Tall Building Structures*. MGB Architecture + Design, Vancouver, 2012

Ed. Bernheimer A. - *Timber in the City: Design & Construction in Mass Timber*. New York, Oro Editions, 2014

Green M., Taggart J. - *Tall Wood Buildings - Design, Construction and Performance*. Basel: Birkhäuser Verlag GmbH, 2017

Chapter 13 - The Passive Timber House

Why choose Passivhaus? London, Passivhaus Trust, 2013

Chapter 14 - The Future Timber House

Ed. Kaufmann H., Nerdinger W. - *Building with Timber - Paths into the Future*. London: Prestel, 2011

Ed. Menges A., Schwinn T., Krieg O.D. - *Advancing Wood Architecture - A Computational Approach*. London: Routledge 2017